QU

CALORIE COUNTING

Gill MacLennan

BBC Books

To my husband and best friend Martin, for compiling all the calorie charts for me; for being such a whizz on the computer; for trying all the recipes in the book (even the vegetables); for countless trips to the park with the wee ones at weekends and all the extra hours of storytelling at bedtime while I was cooking and writing. Thank you.

To my mum, for double testing all the recipes with great enthusiasm and efficiency; for trying out new ideas so gamely and for confirming that all the ingredients are easy to buy in Inverness. My biggest fan and fiercest critic. Thank you.

To the team at BBC Books, especially to Heather Holden-Brown for asking me to write this book and to Charlotte Lochhead for her thorough but thoughtful editing. Thank you.

Published by BBC Books,
a division of BBC Enterprises Limited,
Woodlands, 80 Wood Lane
London W12 0TT

First Published 1995

ISBN 0 563 37031 9
Designed by David Robinson
Set in Ehrhardt
Printed and bound in Great Britain by
Richard Clays Ltd, St Ives plc
Jacket illustration by Catherine L Slade

ABOUT THE AUTHOR

Gill MacLennan is Scottish, thirtysomething and has been a cookery writer for over 15 years. She studied Home Economics in Aberdeen, specialising in food and nutrition, before starting her career as a writer on *Family Circle* followed by *Woman's Realm*. She has worked on several top-selling women's magazines and was Cookery Editor of *Woman* for 5 years. She has appeared several times on BBC's *Bazaar* programme and has presented a cookery programme for BBC Scotland. A working mother with three pre-school children, Gill and her family live in Hampton, Middlesex.

General note
All the recipes and information in this book have been double-checked and approved by a qualified nutritionist.

The calorie values have been taken from a computer database based on American research and from McCance and Widdowson's *The Composition of Foods*, fifth edition. You will see that for the very precise measures used in the charts 100g (3½oz) is given. In the recipes however the standard of 100g (4oz) is used. In addition, I've used the manufacturers' nutritional information on the labels of the cans and packets of food I bought for testing the recipes.

CONTENTS

INTRODUCTION

This is not a diet book. It's a book for lovers of good food who care about their weight. I love food and I believe that life's too short to eat bland, boring foods – or worse – to eat foods that you don't like.

The recipes in this book have all been tried and thoroughly tested, and are deliberately bursting with flavour. I've used intense, concentrated, come-alive combinations so that although you are trying to eat less, what you do eat is wonderful and worth sitting down for.

All the recipes are for a single portion, unless it makes more sense, practically, to cook more than one portion and save the rest for another day. They are all calorie-counted but note that the counts given do not account for any serving suggestions mentioned. All are quick to cook because the less time you spend in the kitchen, the less time you are exposed to temptations.

The book is also peppered with tips and hints on choosing food, cooking food and eating less. These tips are the result of years of experience – both mine and those of my friends – and are passed on with the sincere hope that they will save you some time on your road to a weight you feel comfortable with.

The idea behind this book is that you don't diet. You simply learn to choose the lower calorie foods more often than their higher calorie cousins. You should avoid feeling so ravenous that you could eat anything, although reminding ourselves what it is like to be tummy-rumblingly hungry is probably good practice for most of us.

The calorie charts which start on page 28 are designed so that the lowest calorie options in any food category are at the top of the chart and the high calorie choices are lower down. That way, when choosing, for example, a cheese to eat, you can immediately see which are the best choices. Aim for the top.

Gill MacLennan

A personal note

I do not like skimmed milk, cottage cheese or, horror of horrors, Quark. I have tried hard but the difference between them and their full fat versions is too great. I have opted instead for a half-way solution. I would rather drink a small glass of half-fat milk than a large glass of skimmed. Give me half an ounce of buttery fresh Parmesan rather than two ounces of cottage cheese any day. In short, I have used what I like to eat in my recipes and have counted the calories accordingly. If you genuinely like the very low fat versions then swap them in. The important thing is that you make some effort to cut down the amount of fat you eat, and you enjoy eating the end result.

All of the recipes have been computer analysed to check their calorie and fat contents. Eaten with their serving suggestions, they can be enjoyed as part of a low fat lifestyle – whatever your weight. Read, cook and enjoy eating the recipes. I do.

Eating less fat

According to the World Health Organisation's recommendations, we should aim to get less than 30 per cent of our total energy (our total calories) from fat. Most of this should come from unsaturated fats like sunflower and olive oil. In my recipes I use mainly olive oil but I occasionally use unsalted Dutch butter because it has a good flavour.

What is a calorie?

A calorie is a unit of energy. If you were to lie flat all day and not move, your body would need around 1500 calories – 1500 units of energy – just to keep your heart pumping and all the internal organs working. The heavier you are, the more calories you use up in this way. If you ate food with 1500 calories in it and didn't move, your weight would stay the same. If you ate food with more than 1500 calories in it, your body would store the calories it didn't need. It would convert most of them into fat and store them in your body as a reserve for another day. If you ate more than 1500 calories every day over a long period of time and simply stayed still, your body would build up that fat and you would slowly put on weight. To get rid of this weight, you'd have to eat less than your body really needed so that your body would dip into its fat reserves. That way the fat would be used to provide the extra calories your body needs to keep going. Most people need between 1900 to 2500 calories every day to maintain their weight – more if you do regular exercise.

Most of us, of course, don't lie in bed all day. We get up and do things. The more active we are, the more energy we need – the more calories we use up.

Making Choices

Once you understand the calorie counts in different foods, it's up to you to make the right choices. Let's take an example. It's a couple of hours until supper time and you are feeling peckish. You opt for a chocolate bar which gives you 300 calories. However, you could get those 300 calories from 2 apples, 2 oranges *and* 1 banana. You probably think that eating 5 pieces of fruit is an outrageous amount. But why not? If you ate all this fruit, you would feel satisfied because your tummy would have some bulk to work on, you would have satisfied your sweet tooth, you would take in a good range of nutrients and you would have eaten foods low in fat and high in fibre. Now that you know you can trade that one bar of chocolate for half the fruit bowl – can you really choose the chocolate? The choice is yours.

Cutting Down on Calories

Fat

The easiest way to save calories is to eat less fat in your food, both the sort you can see like butter, margarine and the white bit on a chop and the sort that's hidden, in biscuits, pastries and mayonnaise. Aim to:

- Use less butter or margarine
- Use low fat spread instead of butter or margarine
- Use skimmed or semi-skimmed milk instead of whole milk
- Use low-fat yoghurt and fromage frais in place of cream
- Grill rather than fry

- Cut all visible fat from meat
- Choose chicken and fish rather than red meats
- Choose lean beef rather than lamb or pork
- Choose lean cuts rather than sausages and beefburgers
- Eat less hard cheese and less full fat and medium fat cheeses
- Choose low fat soft cheese like cottage cheese rather than hard cheeses
- Eat fresh fruit rather than biscuits or puddings
- Choose sorbet or reduced fat 'ice-creams' rather than traditional dairy ice-cream
- Take the skin off chicken or turkey
- Go easy on pastry, mayonnaise, fried foods, pâtés and salamis, crisps and nuts

Sugar

Sugar provides empty calories. That is, just calories and no goodness. It rots your teeth and your body just does not need it.

Banning the sugar bowl should be your first step. Cut down then cut out sugar in tea or coffee. Train yourself to do with less sweetness. Aim to:

- Use sweeteners rather than sugar but it's best to do without
- Drink plain or fizzy water rather than sweetened fizzy drinks
- If you can't do without the sweetness then drink diet fizzy drinks rather than traditional versions. Diet drinks have a fraction of the calories

- Choose plain unsweetened breakfast cereal rather than the obviously sugared varieties. Check the labels
- Choose reduced sugar jams and marmalades rather than traditional ones and spread thinly. Look out for low sugar fruit spreads
- Choose fruit canned in fruit juice rather than those canned in syrup
- Check the labels of everything you buy. Glucose, fructose, sucrose and dextrose are all sugar in another form. They all provide empty calories and rot your teeth
- Don't be fooled by honey. It may be natural but it's still relatively high in calories with no useful extra goodness
- Eat fewer cakes, especially those with sugary icings. Save them for special occasions
- Cut down on sweets, biscuits or chocolate
- Use sweeteners with added flavour like maple syrup, malt extract, rosehip syrup and honey, especially those with a distinctive taste like Greek Mountain honey so you use less

Fibre

Fibre is the part of a food that your body can't digest and so it gets rid of it. An apple has fibre, apple juice does not. Fibre helps the digestive system work healthily and helps lower the amount of cholesterol in your blood. Eating fibre is a way of enjoying the satisfaction of eating food while knowing that some of the food will go down the loo, not onto your tummy or your hips.

- Brown breads are a very good way to eat fibre. Choose them rather than white breads. Highest in fibre is wholemeal bread then brown, Granary or white with grains
- If you only like white bread choose white with grains rather than plain white bread. But don't worry. White bread has some B vitamins, iron and calcium added to it so it's fairly nutritious
- Eat baked potatoes in their skins rather than boiled potatoes without
- Eat more baked beans, beans and lentils
- Choose a breakfast cereal with bran in it or one of the wholewheat varieties

Making it Easy for Yourself

Shopping

Be strong at the supermarket. It's much easier to resist the temptation to put something in your trolley than to resist the temptation to eat it once you've got it home. *If you don't buy it, you can't eat it.* Aim to:

- Never shop when you are hungry
- Never shop when you are cross or upset
- Draw up a shopping list and stick to it. It will save you time and money
- Try setting yourself a time limit in the supermarket and race to do your shopping against the clock

- Do not wander up and down the aisles looking for inspiration.
- Avoid the aisles that sell chocolates, biscuits and cakes
- Send a partner with a list to do the shopping for you
- Shop with a calorie-conscious (strong-willed) friend and be strong for each other
- Shop with a healthy-eating friend. You'll be too embarrassed to put anything fattening or unhealthy in your basket

Eating

If you have been overweight for some time, you probably eat even when you are not hungry. In fact, you may have completely lost touch with what it is like to feel hungry. People eat for lots of reasons, because they are happy – or sad, because they are bored or lonely, because they are angry or upset, through habit or because they enjoy eating.

If you feel like eating but you are not really tummy-rumblingly hungry then *do not go into the kitchen*. Instead:

- Brush your teeth. It's amazing how that minty flavour puts you off eating – and think of the money you'll save next time you visit the dentist
- Go for a walk. Put your trainers on, put the dog on a lead or the baby in the buggy and go round the block. Stay out for at least 20 minutes and try to walk so fast that your breathing speeds up

- Drink a pint of water. No rush, take it slowly, put in lots of ice cubes. It'll take the edge off your appetite. It'll also make you wee a lot but it's good for your skin and most of us don't drink enough anyway
- Put on that exercise video. The one that's gathering dust above *The Jungle Book* and *When Harry Met Sally*. Get your trainers and your comfy tracksuit bottoms or a pair of leggings on and don't just sit there – do what the lady says
- Phone a friend
- Work out what you are hungry for, choose something you really want to eat, sit down and enjoy it. Don't stand at the fridge door hoovering up everything in sight – try one of the five points suggested above.

Treating Yourself

It's the food that you eat most of the week that will decide whether you are fat or not. You can't come to too much harm if one meal out of the 21 you eat in the week is higher in calories than the rest of the food you enjoy.

- If you always have fish and chips on a Friday night, then carry on and enjoy them. But when the fish fryer asks if you want a large or a medium haddock, say a small one. Firmly. (You've just saved yourself a few hundred calories.) Large or small chips? The answer's small. You might even try not eating the skin and the batter on the base of the fish. And you could always share a bag of chips

- If you always go to the pub on a Saturday night, then carry on but say no to the crisps and peanuts
- If you always have a roast dinner on a Sunday, then carry on and enjoy it. But help yourself to extra portions of vegetables rather than extra roast potatoes. And try and choose the fruit salad for pudding, not the apple pie and custard.

Adapting Your Lifestyle

If you can't drink tea or coffee through the day without eating biscuits then don't switch the kettle on. Swap to drinking water and eating fruit. Your skin will improve within the week. Aim to:

- Not eat while watching television
- Not eat while standing up
- Not eat in front of the fridge
- Drink a large glass of chilled water while you are waiting for your meal to cook
- Stay out of the kitchen while you are waiting for your meal to cook
- Serve your meals on a smaller plate as it makes the helping look more generous
- Choose the vegetables first and be generous with them. Then choose what you'll have with them
- Sip a warm cup of fruit or herb tea, black tea or coffee or a yeast extract drink if you think you might nibble. All are calorie free.

It's not what you eat but how much you eat.

When you think of all the books that have been written about losing weight, you'd think there was a great secret behind it. The truth is, it's quite straightforward. To lose weight, you have to eat less or exercise more. It's no more difficult – or easy – than that and, whichever way you look at it, if you are overweight and unhappy about it you have to make an effort to do one or the other. (If you do both together, the results will be even quicker.)

The Facts

People are fat for all sorts of different reasons. Over the years I've come to realise that we are all born with a particular constitution and a build and there's no point in fighting it. It's in your genes. If you come from a family with short legs, then nothing in the world is going to make you grow up like a leggy model or a six-foot pole vaulter. You can wear high heels, platform soles or put 'lifts' in your boots, but at the end of the day you look like a person with short legs and tall footwear.

The same applies to people who are overweight. Our bodies use up food at a different rate. People who seem to be able to eat a lot and stay slim have a higher metabolic rate than those who don't eat very much but still gain weight. However, unlike the length of your legs, you can do something about it. You can raise the rate at which your body uses calories – increase your metabolic rate – by taking regular exercise. By doing so, your body will use up calories more efficiently, breaking down your fat reserves, and you'll be able to lose weight faster. (It's really worth making the effort because you'll definitely feel happier, more positive and more energetic after exercise.)

If you can't be bothered to get out of puff a few times a week by walking briskly, swimming or taking an exercise class, then you are stuck with losing weight by eating less. Now if you are the sort of person who can eat 3 Big Macs, 12 roast potatoes or a whole strawberry cheesecake at any one sitting, then you deserve to look like a Sumo wrestler. All you have to do is eat less – reduce your intake to 1 Big Mac, 6 roast potatoes or half a strawberry cheesecake – and you will lose weight. If this sounds like you, then you'll lose weight quickly just by starting to eat sensibly. If you are overweight but generally eat a healthy diet, then *it's not what you are eating, but how much of it you are eating*. Which brings me back to calories.

When it comes to eating, you can eat very small quantities of things that have a lot of calories in them, or you can eat reasonable quantities of foods that have fewer calories in them. Ideally, to lose weight, you should eat foods that are low in fat, low in sugar and high in fibre. *And if you are going to be successful in keeping your weight under control forever, you have to eat low fat, low sugar, high fibre foods, most of the time, for the rest of your life.*

A lot of people think of a diet as something they 'go on' for a short time – 2 weeks, 3 months, a year – in order to become slimmer. Once they have achieved their dream weight they 'come off' the diet and revert to normal eating practices. However, if this way of eating was what made you overweight in the first place then the pounds will pile straight back on. Unless you learn to enjoy the foods you eat 'on a diet', unless it becomes an easy way of life for you and you can continue to eat like this forever, it can't do you any real good.

Getting slimmer is possible for everyone. Admittedly some people find it easier than others but once you understand about calories, understand about which foods to choose, understand that you can cook delicious meals, eat well and not feel hungry, you are in a far better position to lose weight and keep it off. Start today.

- Most women will lose weight eating 1,200 calories a day although 1,500 is easier to stick to. Most men will shift the excess on 1,500 but 1,800 will see results too. Don't try to eat 1,000 calories or less. Your body thinks it's being starved and starts to conserve its calorie reserves (fat).

Five Easy Things to do to Lose Weight

If you do all five of the following, I can guarantee that you will lose weight:

Drink more water

Water is free of calories. If you live somewhere where the water tastes horrible, you should drink a 1.5 litre bottle of mineral water every day. Keep it in the fridge. If you are lucky enough to be able to drink it from the tap, have six mugfuls of water every day. Start at breakfast and have a glass every few hours.

Eat more vegetables

Eating more vegetables is one of the keys to healthy eating. Apart from the fact that they are full of goodness, they fill you up without adding lots of calories to your diet. Don't feed yourself tired old veggies that have been lurking at the bottom of the vegetable rack for a week. Treat yourself to the freshest, best quality you can afford. Choose the smallest, most tender ones for the best flavour, cook them lightly or eat them raw, but make sure you have at least 4 portions every day. A portion is about 100g (4oz).

Eat more fruit

Full of goodness and natural sweetness, fruit offers a range of tastes and textures. Don't get stuck with the fruit bowl staples – treat yourself to the range of fresh fruit in season and you'll never get bored. Fruit is a good source of fibre and is low fat. Aim to eat 4 portions a day of about 100g (4oz) each.

Eat more slowly

Did your mum ever tell you to chew your food 30 times before you swallowed? Mine did. Try it. With every mouthful from now on. It's quite hard to really concentrate on the food and keep it in your mouth for that long. Don't add more food until the first mouthful has gone. And try counting to 5 slowly between mouthfuls. If you are eating with someone, try to be the last one finished. Be aware of what you are eating, and what it tastes like. Learn to savour your food, not bolt it down without noticing.

Take some exercise

I don't mean start playing squash or go cross-country running. I don't even mean signing up for aerobics classes. I mean the sort of exercise you can do every day. Twenty minutes of really vigorous housework like polishing the windows will use up the same number of calories as 20 minutes of horse riding or rock climbing and, if you are at home, it's a lot easier to organise. Ten minutes or so pedalling fast on your bike will use up as many calories as 30 minutes at a stretch class. If you are short of time, it might be easier for you to cycle to the shops or to the station rather than get yourself to a sports centre or a church hall for a stretch class. To get fitter and to kick-start your metabolism into using up more calories, you've got to do a little more exercise for a longer period every day, forever more. Here are some helpful hints:

- Try walking quicker and walking further. Get off the bus a stop earlier than you usually do and try to beat the bus to your regular stop. Don't walk the most direct way to the station in the mornings – take the scenic route and stretch your legs. Don't buy a paper at the nearest newsagents. Order it from a shop that's far enough away for you to get a good walk on your way to collect it
- Try to walk so fast that your breathing speeds up. Breathe air in through your nose and breathe out through your mouth
- Avoid escalators and lifts, unless you are pushing a buggy, and use the stairs
- Volunteer to walk a neighbour's dog
- Get the bike out of the shed and go round the block on it twice a night. Buy yourself a milometer and a speedometer. Take a note of how fast you cycle today and how long it took. Then do it faster tomorrow or cycle further. You don't have to cycle for miles. Better to do half a mile every day than do 4 miles once, have your muscles seize up and leave your poor bike to a slow puncture in the shed
- Get the swimsuit out and swim a few lengths,

every week. Swimming is great exercise for people of all ages and all weights. Join a water aerobics class and let the water take the strain. Who knows, you might even enjoy it.

The following chart is a guide to how many calories you can use up by adding sport or everyday physical activities to your daily routine. Don't just read it. Choose what you are going to do tomorrow and do it. You aren't going to lose weight unless you make some effort. The calories you use up will depend on how much energy you expend. Twenty minutes swimming from one end of the pool to the next doing a leisurely breast stroke is a good start. Twenty minutes non-stop, in lanes, doing a fast crawl is better. Half an hour desperately trying to stay upright on ice-skates will use up some extra calories and might be fun. Thirty minutes doing a Torvill-and-Dean routine will use up more energy. Are you getting the picture?

The other thing to bear in mind is the amount of time you can spend on any one activity. Golf might seem a poor option at only 4 calories a minute but when 9 holes can take at least 1 hour 45 minutes and 18 holes upwards of 3½ hours, it starts to seem like good exercise for people who can spare the time.

Activity	*Calories burned off per minute*	*Activity*	*Calories burned off per minute*
Squash	10	Disco dancing	5
Step exercises	8	Football	5
Climbing stairs	8	Ice- or roller-skating	5
Running	8	Mowing the grass	5
Aerobics class	7	Table tennis	5
Cycling	7	Digging the garden	4
Jogging	7	Golf	4
Swimming	7	Judo	4
Weightlifting	7	Horse-riding	4
Rugby	6	Housework	4
Skipping	6	Rock climbing	4
Tennis	6	Cricket	3
Badminton	5	Ironing	3
Basketball	5	Stretch class	3
Circuit training in a gym	5	Walking	2

Your Ideal Weight

I would say that your ideal weight is the weight that you feel most comfortable at. When you feel comfortable, you feel confident; when you feel confident, you feel happy, and when you feel happy, life's a breeze.

Doctors use charts worked out by insurance companies to ascertain if you are overweight or not. They usually give a broad band of weights that are considered normal for a person of a certain height.

These take into account 'heavy bones' and a big frame. If you are overweight, you need only be concerned if your weight is above the *maximum* recommendation for your height. (Doctors are sure that even half a stone above your recommended weight can have an affect on medical conditions like high blood pressure and high blood cholesterol levels.) Look up your height in the charts below and if you are still in doubt, take all your clothes off and stand in front of a full-length mirror. If any bits look lumpy, wobbly or saggy then fewer calories and a bit of exercise are in order.

On the whole we are, as a nation, getting fatter. Clothes manufacturers tell us that women today

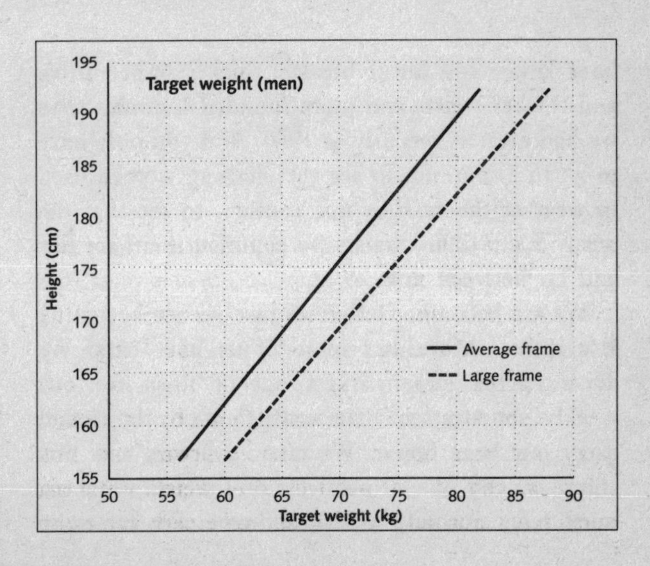

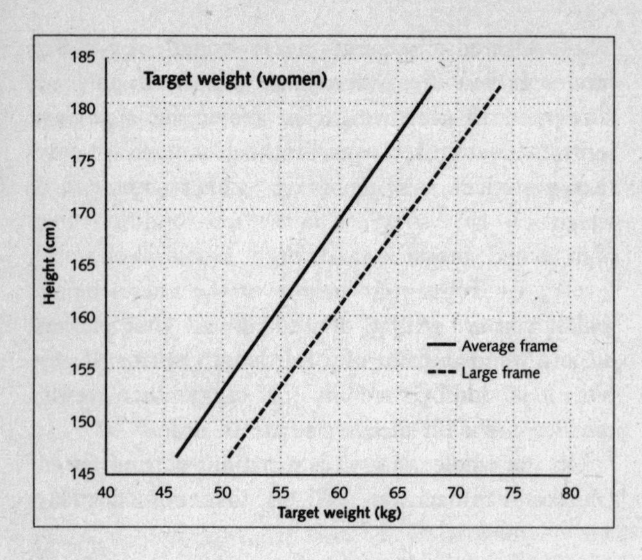

have larger and lower breasts, thicker upper arms, and thicker waists and more rounded tummies than we had even as recently as 1950. And you only have to go to a museum to see the clothing women used to wear at the turn of this century, to see that the wispy 50cm (20in) waists (so common then) are few and far between now.

We are becoming fatter because we are becoming less active. More and more of us have cars. We drive to big supermarkets out of town for our weekly shop rather than walk to local shops and carry our bags home. We take escalators and lifts where we can. We sit passively on the sofa watching more television and videos at home. We eat more manufactured and processed foods laden with fats and sugars. We eat more high fat take-away foods and we even get them delivered. In short, it's not only the food that we eat but also the lifestyle that we lead which is contributing to keeping us fat.

Being Practical

Understanding about calories is a huge step to choosing the right foods, but I think calorie counts should be treated as guides and you shouldn't worry about the odd 50 here and there. After reading this book you should develop a calorie awareness and it is this awareness that will help you to lose weight and keep that weight off. Use the calorie charts as guides. If most of the food you eat comes from the top half of the calorie charts (see page 28) you shouldn't go far wrong and you should be able to count calories sensibly to lose weight. Aim for a daily figure, give or take 100 or so calories. Don't get obsessed and let it take over your life but do be aware of what you are eating. Remember, it is more often than not the *quantity* of food you are eating, not the *type* of food that is the problem.

Write down everything you eat over the next 3 days. Then look everything up in the calorie charts and calculate your total. To start to lose weight you will have to eat less than this number of calories (or eat the same number but take more exercise to burn the weight off). Combine both options and the weight loss will be much more rapid.

To lose 450g (1lb) of body fat you must reduce your calorie intake by 3,500 calories over a period of time. If you usually eat around 2,500 calories a day, and you cut back to around 2,000 calories a day then after a week you will have 'saved' 500 calories a day i.e. around 3,500 calories or 450g (1lb) of fat. (Your body will dip into its fat reserves to provide you with the extra energy you are missing.)

Setting Goals

I'm all for the easy life. I'd rather lose a steady ½kg (1lb) every week and eat a reasonable amount of food than hope to lose 1kg (2lbs) a week on a regime which I couldn't keep up. We are talking about eating habits here – long-term changes – and my experience suggests that taking things steadily and slowly does the trick. Take a deep breath and, if you have that much to lose, plan to be 5kg or 1 stone lighter, forever, 3 months from today. Then review the situation and if you have more to lose, set yourself a new goal.

What you should aim for is to take in fewer calories than you need but not so much fewer that you feel hungry and light-headed. The number of calories you need will depend on whether you are male or female, how active a life you lead and how much weight you have to lose. Most women will lose weight eating 1,200 calories a day, although 1,500 is easier to stick to. Most men will shift the excess on 1,500 but 1,800 will see results, too, and be easier to stick to even if it takes a tiny bit longer. Don't try to eat less than 1,000 calories a day. It's impossible to keep it up and your body thinks it's being starved and starts to conserve its calorie reserves just in case it needs them, which is rather counter productive. Aim to eat 7 times your chosen daily calorie intake, divided up over a week – you may eat more calories over the weekend and be able to eat less through the week, but as long as *on average* you stick to your total weekly figure you should see some progress.

It's probably taken you some time to become overweight so it is unreasonable to expect to be thin by 2 weeks on Saturday. (If you have a party or a special function 2 weeks on Saturday and you can't get into anything, then buy yourself a larger frock or pair of trousers and enjoy the occasion in comfort. Don't abuse your body by starving it for 2 weeks and yo-yoing back to fatness afterwards.)

By the way, most fat people have at some time wondered if – nay hoped – they had a dodgy thyroid. (Your thyroid is a gland in you neck which regulates growth.) For most of us this is as hopeless as dreaming about winning £1,000,000 when we don't even do the Pools. Thyroid conditions are rare so you are stuck with eating low calorie foods and taking exercise if you want to lose weight.

Armed with knowledge about calorie content of food and how to ward off hunger, feeling satisfied and eating well is possible and enjoyable.

CALORIE CHARTS

Basics

For this section only, I have chosen to list the ingredients alphabetically. This is because it's highly unlikely that you would substitute dried herbs for cooking chocolate just because they had fewer calories.

Anchovy essence, 1 teaspoon	5
Anchovy fillet canned in oil, 1 drained	5
Apple sauce, 1 tablespoon	19
Baking powder, 1 teaspoon	5
Barbecue sauce, 1 tablespoon	15
Black bean sauce, 1 tablespoon	25
Capers, 1 teaspoon, drained	6
Chilli, 1 average fresh	2
Chocolate, cooking, 28g (1oz)	155
Cocoa powder, 1 teaspoon	9
Coconut, creamed, 28g (1oz)	96
Coconut, fresh, 28g (1oz)	99
Coffee and chickory essence, 1 teaspoon	10
Coffee, instant, 2 teaspoons	0
Cornflour, 1 tablespoon	30
Cranberry jelly, 28g (1oz)	42
Cranberry sauce, 1 tablespoon	20
Curry paste, 1 teaspoon	7
Curry powder, 1 teaspoon	10
Custard powder, 1 tablespoon	30
Fish sauce (Chinese/Thai) 1 tablespoon	3
French dressing, 1 teaspoon	77
Garam masala, 1 teaspoon	15
Gelatine, 10g sachet	34

Ground black pepper	0
Herbs, dried or fresh, all kinds	0
Horseradish sauce, 1 teaspoon	5
Jam, 1 teaspoon	15
Mango chutney, 1 tablespoon	38
Marmalade, 1 teaspoon	15
Marzipan, 28g (1oz)	130
Mayonnaise, low cal., 1 tablespoon	35
Mayonnaise, 1 tablespoon	110
Mint jelly, 1 tablespoon	37
Mint sauce, 1 tablespoon	5
Miso, 1 tablespoon	33
Mustard, made English, 1 teaspoon	10
Mustard, Dijon, 1 teaspoon	10
Mustard, German, 1 teaspoon	8
Olives, 1 black	3
Olives, 1 stuffed	5
Oyster sauce, 1 tablespoon	10
Paprika, 1 teaspoon	9
Peanut butter, 28g (1oz)	165
Redcurrant jelly, 28g (1oz)	45
Salad cream, 1 tablespoon	48
Salad cream, low cal., 1 tablespoon	18
Soy sauce, light, 1 tablespoon	8
Soy sauce, dark, 1 tablespoon	15
Spices, dried, all kinds	0
Stock cubes, each cube	28
Tomato ketchup, 1 tablespoon	15
Treacle, 1 teaspoon	17
Worcestershire sauce, 1 tablespoon	12

Basics continued

For this and all the calorie charts that follow, I have listed the ingredients with the lowest calorie options at the top of the charts in each section.

Flour – for 28g (1oz)

Wholemeal, self-raising	81
Wholemeal, organic	88
Wholemeal	90
Plain white, organic	95
Strong white (for bread)	95
Cornflour	95
Rye	96
Soft white (for cakes)	99
Plain white	100
Granary	100
Rice flour	100
Soya flour, low fat	101
Soya flour	126

Pickles – for 28g (1oz)

Gherkins	3
Mixed pickle	5
Red cabbage	6
Pickled onions	6
Baby beets	13
Beetroot in vinegar	15
Piccalilli, sweet	25
Cocktail onions	30
Sweet pickle	39
Lime pickle	75

Sugars – for 28g (1oz)	
Dark soft brown sugar	108
Light soft brown sugar	109
Brown crystals	112
Glucose	112
Caster sugar	114
White granulated	114
Demerara sugar	114
Icing sugar	114

Syrups and Treacles – for 2 tablespoons	
Rosehip syrup	65
Maple syrup	70
Grenadine	72
Black treacle	75
Molasses	80
Honey	82
Golden syrup	85
Malt extract	90

• All sugar has more or less the same calories. The advantage that the soft brown sugars has over their refined white cousins is flavour. You need to use less to get the same amount of sweetness.

Biscuits

Sweet Biscuits – for 1 biscuit of the most famous brand

Rich Tea	33
Lemon Puff	35
Malted Milk	38
Garibaldi	40
Nice	43
Ginger Nut	47
Jaffa Cake	47
Shortcake	50
Fig Roll	52
Custard Cream	53
Gipsy Cream	67
Bourbon Cream	68
Digestive	73
Chocolate Hob Nob	80
Jammie Dodger	84
Chocolate Homewheat	85
Shortbread Finger	104
Caramel Wafer	125

Savoury Biscuits and Crispbreads – for 1 biscuit of the most famous brand

Melba toasts	15
Grissini (Italian bread stick)	15
High fibre crackerbread	20
Wheaten crackers	21
High bake water biscuit	22
Original or brown Ryvita	26
Sesame seed Ryvita	30

Rice cakes	30
Cream cracker	32
Wholemeal cracker	38
Butter puff	45
Wholemeal bran biscuit	60

Bread

Loaves – for 28g (1oz)

Pumpernickel	60
Wholemeal (100%)	61
Brown Granary bread	63
Wholemeal Granary or brown	63
White, soft grain	64
Bran bread	65
Wheatgerm (Hovis and VitBe)	65
White	66
Granary	70
Light rye	70
Malt loaf	70
Ciabatta	73
Soda bread, white	75
Milk loaf	80
French bread	85
Foccaccia	93
Enriched (Cholla, Brioche)	110

Rolls and Bread Products – each

Crumpet, 40g (1½oz)	75
Scotch pancake	80
Muffin, 60g (2¼oz)	125

Bread continued

Wholemeal bap, 40g (1½oz)	125
Wholemeal roll, 50g (1¾oz)	125
White bap, 40g (1½oz)	130
Dinner roll, 40g (1½oz)	130
Soft brown roll, 45g (1¾oz)	140
Crusty roll, brown or white, 45g (1¾oz)	145
Soft white roll, 45g (1¾oz)	150
Bagel, 40g (1½oz)	150
Scone, wholemeal, fruit, 55g (2oz)	150
Scone, white, 55g (2oz)	160
Croissant, 40g (1½oz)	165
Pitta bread, wholemeal, 60g (2½oz)	165
Pitta bread, white 60g (2½oz)	180
Scone, white, fruit, 75g (3oz)	210
Brioche roll, 45g (1¾oz)	215
Granary bap, large, 60g (2½oz)	200
Chapati	255
Croissant, 60g (2½oz)	280
Naan, small 110g (4¼oz)	330
Paratha	450

Breakfast Cereal – *for 28g (1oz)*

Weetabix (for 1 biscuit)	65
All Bran	76
Sultana Bran	81
Rice Krispies	90
Cornflakes	90
Muesli, unsweetened	97
Muesli, traditional	103

Alpen	104
Sugar Puffs	105
Coco Pops	107
Frosties	107
Special K	107
Ricicles	107
Porridge oats	107
Oatmeal	114
Crunchy Oat Cereal	118

Butter, Margarine and Oils – *for 28g (1oz)*
From a calorie point of view there is no difference between saturated and unsaturated fat.

4g (⅛oz) butter or margarine	28
8g (¼oz) butter or margarine	56
1 teaspoon oil	45
Very low fat spreads	75
Low fat spreads	111
Butter, all types	210
Margarine	210
Beef suet, shredded	235
Vegetable suet, shredded	235
Sesame oil	246
Concentrated butter	247
Dripping	253
Solid vegetable oil	255
Oils, all types: olive, sunflower, corn, safflower, vegetable etc.	255
Lard	255
Ghee	257

Cheese

Look out for individually wrapped portions of cheese, often sold as pick'n'mix in supermarkets. They offer the advantage of a selection of tastes but in calorie-controlled portions. The new, 'healthy' sunflower oil cheeses, while higher in unsaturated fat, which is better for you, contain as many calories as traditional cheese. A good tip for counting your calories is to grate a large block of cheese in the food processor and weigh it into 25g (1oz) portions. Line a 12 hole bun tin with cling film and put 1 portion of cheese in each and freeze.

Cutting Cheeses – for 28g (1oz)

Feta (Danish cows')	73
Austrian smoked	78
Halumi	84
Camembert	85
Feta (Greek ewes')	85
Blue Brie	88
Brie	89
Mozzarella	90
Processed	90
Edam	91
Parmesan, fresh	92
Port Salut	94
Roquefort	95
Danish Blue	97
Dolcellata	100
White Stilton	101
Lancashire	104

Caerphilly	105
Cheshire	106
Emmental	106
Wensleydale	106
Gouda	110
Gorgonzola	112
Derby	112
Leicester	112
Double Gloucester	113
Blue Stilton	115
Cheddar	115
Gruyère	117
Parmesan, dried, grated	210

Soft Cheeses – for 28g (1oz)

Quark skimmed milk cheese	20
Cottage cheese, reduced fat	21
Cottage cheese, plain	27
Quark low fat cheese	35
Quark medium fat cheese	45
Ricotta	48
Curd cheese	54
Goats' milk soft cheese	55
Full fat soft cheese	87
Bel Paese	96
Mascarpone	112
Boursin	115
Cream cheese	122

Chicken, Turkey, Duck, Goose and Game

For 28g (1oz). Figures quoted are for skinless cuts unless otherwise stated. If you choose to include the skin calories increase by between a third and a half again.

Chicken drumstick, with bone, grilled	19
Chicken wing quarter, with bone, roasted	19
Chicken leg quarter, with bone, grilled	21
Chicken thigh, boneless, roasted	21
Chicken breast, with bone, grilled	24
Chicken leg quarter, with bone, roasted	24
Turkey, boneless, skinless, roasted	40
Chicken breast, boneless, roasted	42
Turkey, boneless, skinless, smoked	44
Turkey, boneless with skin, roasted	48
Grouse, boneless, skinless, roasted	49
Chicken breast, boneless, boiled	52
Duck, boneless, skinless, roasted	54
Venison, boneless, skinless, roasted	56
Partridge, boneless, skinless, roasted	60
Chicken breast, boneless, with skin, roasted	61
Pheasant, boneless, skinless, roasted	61
Pigeon, boneless, skinless, roasted	66
Goose, boneless, skinless, roasted	90
Duck, boneless, with skin, roasted	97

Crisps and Nibbles – *for 28g (1oz).*

Watch out! Most nuts are sold in 50g bags so will be roughly twice as many calories as those listed below.

Tropical Nut Mix	55
Raisins	70
Popcorn (plain)	110
Twiglets	114
Peanuts and raisins	116
Yoghurt-coated raisins	125
Ready salted crisps, lower fat	130
Taco crisps or shells	130
Bombay Mix	135
Tortilla chips	137
Trail Mix	140
Java crackers	140
Ocean crunchies	140
Prawn crackers (ready-to-eat)	143
Ready salted crisps – all flavours	145
Banana chips	146
Yoghurt-coated peanuts	155
Hula Hoops	160
Californian corn chips	162
Cheese flavour puffs	168
Cashews, roasted and salted	172
Dry roasted peanuts	174
Pistachios	176
Salted peanuts	182
Pork scratchings	189

(see also Nuts and Seeds page 54)

Dairy

Be aware of the Dairy Ladder:

Butter is 100% fat
Double cream is 48% fat
Whipping cream is 35% fat
Cheddar is 33% fat
Single cream is 18% fat
Half-fat Cheddar is 14% fat
Greek yoghurt (cow's) is 10% fat
Greek yoghurt (sheep's) is 8% fat
Fromage frais is 8% fat
Cottage cheese is 4% fat
Fromage frais is 1% fat
Natural yoghurt is 2% fat
Skimmed milk soft cheese (Quark) is less than 1% fat

Milk – for 284 ml (½ pint)	
Skimmed	98
Instant spray-dried, low fat, skimmed milk	100
Buttermilk	116
Semi-skimmed milk	133
Silver Top, pasteurised, with cream removed	133
Instant dried, skimmed milk with vegetable fat	140
Half-fat milk	165
Evaporated milk, full cream	180
Soya milk	185

Green Top, untreated farm milk	190
Longlife or UHT	190
Organic milk	190
Silver Top, pasteurised	190
Sterilised whole milk	190
Goats' milk	207
Gold Top	223
Condensed, unsweetened	400
Evaporated	450
Condensed, skimmed, sweetened	760
Condensed, full fat, sweetened	910

Cream/yoghurt/fromage frais in handy measures per level tablespoon

Diet fromage frais	7
Virtually fat free natural yoghurt	7
Natural yoghurt	10
Plain fromage frais	16
Strained Greek-style yoghurt	18
Fruit fromage frais	16
Half cream	20
Single cream	27
Fresh soured cream	27
Whipping cream	61
Crème fraîche	63
Double or extra thick double cream	70
Clotted cream	165

Drinks

• *As a rough guide, you can drink 3 shorts to 1 pint of beer or lager. A whisky and soda, a gin and slimline or a rum and diet coke all cost under 60 calories – a pint of beer can cost nearer 200 and, of course, a mineral water is calorie free*

• *Try alternating an alcoholic drink every second round, with a low-calorie soft drink*

• *Buy yourself a drink measure. It is very easy to pour yourself much bigger measures without one*

• *Buy half bottles of wine*

• *Beware: Beers for diabetics are not a low calorie substitute. They contain less sugar but the sugar has been turned to alcohol which often means they are higher in calories than your usual bottle of beer*

• *Beware: Low alcohol drinks often have the same calories as the ordinary drink.*

Alchoholic Drinks – for a pub measure (⅙ of a gill for spirits or standard beer bottle)

Alcohol-free lager (½pt)	50
Dry Martini	50
Gin	55
Brandy	55
Vodka	55
Whisky	55
Pernod	65
Sherry, dry, 2fl oz	66
Babycham, sweet, standard bottle	75
Dubonnet, red	75
Cinzano Rosso and Rosé	75

Sherry, cream sweet, 2fl oz	75
Wine, dry red, 5fl oz	75
Wine, dry white, 5fl oz	78
Martini Rosso	80
Cinzano Bianco	80
Brown Ale, standard bottle	80
Lager, ½pt	83
Bitter, pale ale, ½pt	90
Guinness or stout, standard bottle	105

Hot Drinks – for typical serving sizes, as shown

Tea bag	0
Instant coffee, per rounded teaspoon	0
Lemon, per slice	1
Bovril, per cube	10
Skimmed milk, per 30ml (2 tablespoons)	10
Semi skimmed milk, per 30ml (2 tablespoons)	13
Sugar, 1 teaspoon	16
Cocoa powder, per 2 teaspoons	20
Full fat milk, per 30ml (2 tablespoons)	20
Single cream per 15ml (1 tablespoon)	32
Lemon tea mix, per 2 teapoons	35
Drinking chocolate, per tablespoon	50
Double cream, per 15ml (1 tablespoon)	70
Horlicks, per 28g (1oz)	109
Ovaltine, per 28g (1oz)	109
Cadbury's Chocolate Break, per sachet	115
Instant hot chocolate, per 28g (1oz) sachet	119

Drinks continued

Soft Drinks – for 200ml (7fl oz) serving

Drink	Calories
Diet Coca Cola, Pepsi Cola, Seven Up	0
Energen One Cal drinks (all varieties)	0
Slimline ginger ale, lemonade or tonic	0
Diet Lilt	6
Slimline bitter lemon	6
Slimline shandy drink	12
Sparkling Hypertonic drink	12
Dandelion and burdock	40
Dry ginger ale	44
Fanta lemonade	48
Shandy drink	52
Vimto	52
Indian tonic water	62
Lemonade	62
Carrot juice	63
Fanta orange crush	67
American ginger ale	71
Seven Up	76
Irn-Bru	79
Tizer	79
Traditional lemonade	79
Orangina	80
Coca Cola	82
Apple juice	85
Orange juice	88
Pepsi Cola	88
Cherry Coca Cola	88
Tropical fruit juice	88

Bitter lemon crush	88
Appletise	89
Orange and pineapple juice	90
Sparkling apple or grape juice	92
Pineapple or tropical fruit juice	97
Lilt	97
Blackcurrant with apple juice	100
Five fruit juice	105
Grapefruit juice	106
Ribena sparkling blackcurrant juice drink	106
Prune juice	141
Lucozade	144

Squashes and Cordials – for 28ml (1fl oz) undiluted

Quosh low sugar (range of flavours)	0
Robinsons Special R	1
Kia Ora low calorie orange	5
Ginger or lime juice	23
Lemon barley water	25
Low sugar Ribena Light blackcurrant	28
Ribena Light	28
Grapefruit and pineapple	30
Lemon squash	30
Orange and grapefruit	30
Apple and blackberry	31
Blackcurrant	35
Orange squash	35
Kia Ora high juice orange squash	45
Ribena blackcurrant and apple juice drink	79
Ribena blackcurrant health drink	83

Eggs

Chicken Eggs (raw) – for each egg

White of size 3	14
Yolk of size 3	65
Size 4, whole	75
Size 3, whole	79
Size 2, whole	90
Size 1, whole	95

Chicken Eggs (cooked) – for each size 3 egg

Poached	77
Hard boiled	79
Scrambled with 8g (¼oz) butter	135
Fried in 2 teaspoons oil	170
2-egg omelette with 8g (¼oz) butter	215
2 eggs, scrambled with 8g (¼oz) butter	215

Other Eggs – for medium, raw, egg weight as given

Quails 9g (⅓oz)	14
Duck 70g (2¾oz)	129
Turkey 79g (3oz)	135
Goose 144g (5oz)	266

• Quail's eggs, now widely available in large supermarkets and delicatessens, make a good starter or salad. Soft-boil for about 1 minute then plunge into cold water. Serve in their shells then peel and eat (lightly dipped in salt and ground black pepper) or halve into a salad. You can have 6 quail's eggs in place of 1 hen's egg.

Fish

White Fish – for 100g (3½oz)

Haddock fillets, raw	73
Hake fillets, raw	73
Coley fillets, raw	73
Cod fillets, raw	76
Lemon sole, flesh only, steamed	91
Plaice, flesh only, steamed	91
Whiting, flesh only, steamed	92
Haddock, smoked, steamed	101
Halibut, middle cut, steamed	131
Haddock, crumbed and fried	174
Fish cakes, fried	188
Cod, battered and fried	199
Fish fingers, grilled	214
Fish fingers, fried	233
Taramasalata	446

Oily Fish – for 100g (3½oz)

Tuna, canned in spring water	107
Tuna, canned in brine	113
Pilchards, canned in tomato sauce	126
Trout, flesh only, steamed	135
Salmon, smoked	142
Tuna, canned in oil	161
Sardines, canned in tomato sauce	177
Salmon, raw	182
Salmon, canned	185
Herring, flesh only, grilled	199
Kipper, flesh only, baked	205

Fish continued

Sardines, canned in oil, drained	217
Anchovies, canned in oil	280
Mackerel, smoked, flesh and skin	354
Whitebait, fried	525

Shellfish – for 100g (3½oz)

Cockles, flesh only	48
Mussels, flesh only, boiled	48
Shrimps, peeled	73
Squid, fresh raw	75
Prawns, flesh only, boiled	107
Lobster, flesh only, boiled	119
Crab, flesh only, boiled	127
Scampi, crumbed and fried	316

Fruit

Canned Fruit – for 215g (7½oz) serving

Rhubarb in fruit juice	42
Apple slices in fruit juice	50
Raspberries in fruit juice	64
Rhubarb in syrup	64
Apricot halves in fruit juice	65
Blackberries in fruit juice	76
Peach slices in fruit juice	76
Pears in fruit juice	76
Fruit cocktail in fruit juice	85
Blackcurrants in fruit juice	86
Grapefruit segments in fruit juice	86
Tropical fruit cocktail in fruit juice	94

Grapefruit segments in syrup	97
Pineapple in fruit juice	101
Strawberries in fruit juice	101
Kiwi fruit in fruit juice	105
Golden plums in light syrup	108
Pears in syrup	117
Apricot halves in syrup	130
Pineapple in syrup	133
Fruit cocktail in syrup	139
Raspberries in syrup	150
Mango slices in syrup	154
Plums in syrup	155
Peach slices in syrup	162
Strawberries in syrup	174
Lychees in syrup	185
Prunes in fruit juice	227
Cherries, black in syrup and Kirsch	228
Prunes in syrup	249

Dried Fruit – for 28g (1oz)

Prunes, ready-to-eat, weighed with stones	33
Prunes, weighed with stones	38
Dried apricots, ready-to-eat	40
Dried pears	45
Prunes, pitted	46
Dried apricots	52
Glacé cherries	60
Dried dates, weighed with stones	60
Dried peaches	60
Dried apple rings	65

Fruit continued

Currants	69
Dried dates, weighed without stones	70
Raisins	70
Sultanas	71
Dried dates, chopped and sugar-rolled	77
Yoghurt-coated raisins	110
Banana chips	147
Desiccated coconut	171

Fresh Fruit – for 1 average-sized piece of fruit

Grape	4
Passion fruit	6
Lychee	8
Apricot, 1 whole	10
Date	15
Plum	15
Mandarin, 75g (3oz)	20
Melon, 225g (8oz) slice	32
Kiwi fruit	35
Orange, small, 140g (5oz)	35
Fig	30
Apple, eating, 140g (5oz)	50
Grapefruit, 450g (1lb)	50
Pear, 175g (6oz)	50
Banana, small, 110g (4oz)	55
Peach, 175g (6oz)	55
Orange, medium, 225g (8oz)	60
Pomegranate, 200g (7oz)	65
Orange, large, 275g (10oz)	75

Papaya, 350g (12oz)	80
Apple, cooking, 225g (8oz)	80
Banana, medium, 175g (6oz)	80
Nectarine, 175g (6oz)	80
Banana, large, 200g (7oz)	95
Mango, 275g (10oz)	100

Fresh Fruit – for 28g (1oz)

Rhubarb	2
Lemon, weighed with skin	4
Melon, weighed with skin	4
Raspberries	7
Strawberries	7
Mandarins, weighed with skin	7
Oranges, weighed with skin	7
Pears, weighed with skin and core	8
Plums, weighed with stones	10
Peaches, weighed without stone	10
Oranges, flesh only	10
Passion fruit, flesh only	10
Papaya, flesh only	11
Pineapple, flesh only	13
Grapes, black	14
Guavas, weighed with seeds	16
Kiwi fruit	16
Grapes, green	17
Mango, flesh only	17
Lychees, peeled and stoned	18
Pomegranate, flesh only	20
Banana, flesh only	22

Nuts and Seeds – *for 28g (1oz)*

Chestnuts	50
Chestnut purée	65
Pistachios with shells	95
Coconut, flesh only, fresh	100
Cob nuts	110
Chestnuts, dried	115
Poppy seeds	139
Peanuts, with shells, fresh	143
Walnuts	150
Cashew nuts	160
Mixed nuts, chopped	160
Peanuts, dry roasted, roasted and salted	160
Almonds, shelled, with skins	161
Peanuts, shelled, fresh	162
Sesame seeds	165
Sunflower seeds	170
Coconut, desiccated	170
Peanut butter	175
Pumpkin seeds	175
Pine nuts	178
Almonds, blanched	179
Pine kernels	180
Pistachios, shelled	180
Brazil nuts, shelled	180
Hazelnuts, shelled	180
Almonds, ground	181
Macadamia	185
Coconut, creamed block	191
Pecans	199

Pasta and Noodles – *for 28g (1oz)*

White pasta, dry or fresh, boiled	33
Chinese egg noodles, dry, boiled	33
Egg pasta, dry, boiled	33
Wholewheat, dry, boiled	34
White pasta, fresh, raw	80
Chinese egg noodles, dry	90
Wholewheat pasta, dry, raw	95
White pasta, dry, raw	105
Egg pasta, dry, raw	105

Pulses and Dried Beans – *for 28g (1oz)*

Baked beans in tomato sauce, canned	20
Haricot beans, boiled	25
Cannellini, canned	25
Butter beans, boiled	27
Lentils, boiled	30
Red kidney beans, boiled	30
Chickpeas, boiled	32
Flageolet beans, boiled	32
Soya beans, boiled	45
Borlotti beans, canned	45
Black beans, boiled or canned in brine	45
Red kidney beans, raw	75
Haricot beans, raw	77
Butter beans, dried	77
Lentils, raw	88
Chickpeas, boiled	90
Flageolet beans, raw, dried	98
Soya beans, raw	110

Red Meat

Bacon – for 28g (1oz) raw weight

Bacon chop, well grilled	41
Gammon steaks, lean, grilled	47
Gammon joint, lean, boiled	48
Round bacon steak, well grilled	50
Back rashers, trimmed, no rind	65
Gammon steaks, grilled	65
Middle rashers, no rind	80
Gammon joint, boiled	80
Streaky rashers, rind removed	85

Beef – for 28g (1oz) raw weight

Braising steak, lean	35
Fillet steak, medium grilled	41
Beefburger, low fat, grilled	42
Stewing steak	50
Rump steak, medium grilled	53
Minced beef, extra lean	55
Sirloin steak, medium grilled	56
Beefburger, grilled	57

Lamb – for 28g (1oz) raw weight

Leg, lean only, roasted	55
Minced lamb, lean	60
Shoulder, lean only, roasted	60
Loin chop, lean and fat, grilled	62
Neck fillets, lean and fat	65
Best end neck lamb cutlets, on bone, grilled	85

Leg, lean and fat, roasted	85
Shoulder, lean and fat, roasted	85

Pork – for 28g (1oz) raw weight

Fillet, lean only	35
Leg, boneless, lean only, roasted	35
Pork braising steak, lean	35
Lean minced pork	55
Ground or minced pork	65
Loin chop, boneless, grilled	65
Crackling, (cooked weight)	202

Rice and Grains – *for 28g (1oz)*

Rice, brown, all sorts, boiled	34
Rice, white, all sorts, boiled	35
Rice, wild, all sorts, boiled	50
Wheat bran	58
Millet	96
Quinoa	96
Rice, brown, raw	100
Semolina	100
Sago	101
Wheat germ	102
Barley, pearl, raw	103
Rice, white, raw	103
Couscous	103
Rice, wild, raw	104
Bulghur wheat	104
Popcorn	105
Cornmeal (polenta)	106

Something Sweet

Bought cakes for 2oz

Malt loaf	148
Fruit cake	184
Cherry fruit slab	196
Cherry Genoa	196
Banana cake	206
Madeira cake	208
Dundee cake	210
Sultana cake	210
Christmas cake (with marzipan and icing)	212
Golden syrup cake	226
Jamaica ginger cake	226

Cakes and Buns – for 28g (1oz)

Meringue nest, small, shop-bought	46
Dairy cream choux bun	130
Dairy cream éclair	145

Chocolates – for a bar or item

Nestlé's Milky Bar (small)	65
Mars' Milky Way	116
Cadbury's Curly Wurly	130
Cadbury's Fudge	130
Toblerone (small, 25g)	140
Rowntree's Walnut Whip	165
Cadbury's Buttons	170
Cadbury's Flake	170
Rowntree's tube of Smarties (small)	173

Cadbury's Cream Egg	175
Mars' Maltesers (37g)	177
Cadbury's Turkish Delight	180
Cadbury's Crunchie	195
Cadbury's Peppermint Cream	210
Rowntree's Toffee Crisp	243
Rowntree's Kit Kat (4 finger)	245
Cadbury's Dairy Milk	255
Cadbury's Bournville (50g bar)	255
Cadbury's Whole Nut	255
Rowntree's Lion Bar	258
Mars' Twix	263
Rowntree's Rolo	264
Mars' Galaxy	267
Mars' Bar	266
Mars' Bounty (milk)	274
Mars' Snickers	293
Rowntree's Yorkie	343

Sweets – for each 28g (1oz)

Bassett's Wine Gums	93
Bassett's Jelly Babies	94
Bassett's Fruit Pastilles	95
Rowntree's Polo Mints, tube	105
Keiller's Clear Fruits	106
Keiller's Barley Sugars	107
Bassett's Dolly Mixtures	108
Keiller's Treacle Toffee	113
Keiller's Liquorice Toffee	118
Mars' Opal Fruits	181

Vegetables – *for 28g (1oz) unless otherwise stated*

Globe artichoke	1
Garlic, 1 clove	2
French beans, boiled	2
Celery	2
Cauliflower	3
Chicory	3
Chinese leaves	3
Marrow	3
Courgette	3
Cucumber	3
Lettuce	3
Endive	3
Fennel	4
Aubergine	4
Celeriac	4
Peppers, green or red	4
Pumpkin	4
Radishes	4
Spinach, cooked	4
Tomatoes	4
Watercress	4
Asparagus	5
Jerusalem artichoke	5
Cabbage	6
Swede	6
Turnips	6
Peas	22
Potato, boiled	23
Sweet potatoes	33

Garlic	40
Sweetcorn kernels	40
Red cabbage	6
Alfafa sprouts	7
Runner beans	7
Broccoli	7
Brussels sprouts	7
Carrot	7
Kohlrabi	7
Onion	7
Spinach, raw	7
Beetroot	8
Beansprouts	9
Leeks	9
Mushrooms	9
Corn on the cob, whole	10
Peppers, yellow	10
Waterchestnuts	10
Broad beans, boiled	14
Parsnip	14
Mangetout	19

In handy measures

Celery, per stick, raw	5
Tomato, 1 average	14
Lettuce, 1 whole	15
Pepper, 1 average	17
Corn on the cob, 1 whole	120
Avocado, ½ average	130
Potato, 75g (6oz) with skin, baked	150

ABOUT THE RECIPES

Most people become interested in calorie counting because they want to lose weight which usually means going on a diet which in turn means grapefruit, boiled eggs, cottage cheese and skimmed milk. When did you last think 'I could murder some cottage cheese on crispbread' or 'I'd give my right arm for some plain grilled fish and steamed carrots'? To lose weight permanently you have to eat foods you enjoy – both while you are losing weight and afterwards. As a working mum with a full-time job and 3 pre-school children, I cook simple food which is quick to prepare, easy to cook and will be enjoyed. These recipes taste good and the fact that they are low in calories and low in fat, and part of a healthy eating plan is a big plus. Before you get started let me explain some things about the recipes and the information panels.

Calorie Counts

The calorie counts at the top of each recipe are for the recipe as it is written and don't include the serving suggestions. Remember to add extra calories for the broccoli, rice or whatever. The counts given in the boxes are for one portion only, even if occasionally (as in soups chapter) the recipe makes more than one portion.

Vegetarian Recipes

Vegetarian recipes are marked with the symbol Ⓥ Strict vegetarians who don't eat cheese set with animal rennet should make the appropriate swaps.

Metric and Imperial

The recipes are written with both metric and imperial measures. Please stick to *either* metric *or* imperial when you are cooking. Don't mix the two as they really aren't interchangeable.

Kitchen Scales

You certainly don't need anything costly when you are calorie-counting but kitchen scales are essential. Buy a set that will weigh 15g (½oz) accurately. I have a tiny set in my kitchen which only weighs up to 450g (1lb). I think it's a really good idea to weigh everything when you are starting out – if you don't work with food, you are probably not aware of how much food weighs. Portions such as 25g (1oz) of cheese and a 175g (6oz) portion of boiled pasta can seem alarmingly small. One slice of bread can weigh anything from 25g (1oz) to 50g (2oz), a baked potato could easily weigh 250g (10oz) or more, not the 150g (6oz) allowed for in the recipe. Weight is particularly important when you are using foods that are high in fat. A portion of cheese weighing 25g (1oz) might be 100 calories – a tiny bit more may add on as much as 50 extra calories.

Measuring Spoons

All teaspoons and tablespoons are level. I used a proper set of measuring spoons when I tested the recipes and levelled dry ingredients with the back of a knife.

Measuring spoons are a must, especially for oils and mayonnaise where the calories are very concentrated. They are usually plastic, come in a set of four or five spoons which stack one inside the other, and are joined together by a ring though their handles. They are very inexpensive and are easily available in the supermarket.

Liquidiser

This is invaluable for soups and you get a much better result than if you use a food processor. Mine used to be an attachment to my trusty Kenwood mixer, but I have to confess that the Kenwood is now in a box in the shed and I have a powerful liquidiser on the work top all the time. It's great for shakes – see the Breakfast chapter – and if it is out on the counter, it is always ready to use.

Food Processor

For chopping and grating and for all sorts of food preparation I wouldn't be without my food processor. It's handy for chopping meat for burgers, making purées and sauces and chopping herbs.

Coffee Grinder

I never use mine for grinding coffee. It's handy for grinding spices or for coping with quantities that are too small to put in the food processor. I would say it's not essential but if you got one for a wedding present you could press it into action.

Non-stick Pans

A small non-stick saucepan, a small non-stick omelette pan and a deep-sided non-stick frying-pan for stir-frying are all that you need. They don't have to be expensive, but the pans should feel heavy not lightweight. All of mine came from the supermarket and were picked up with the rest of the shopping. Look for a famous non-stick label and you can't go wrong.

Steamer

I use a colander over a pan of simmering water with an odd pan lid on top but you can buy collapsable metal trays that sit on top of a pan or proper, rigid metal steamers with handles and holes in the bottom that stack on top of each other. Steaming is a great way to cook vegetables and fish.

Microwaves

I have an 800 watt microwave oven. If you have a microwave oven which has a different power, see your manufacturer's handbook to work out the correct cooking times.

BREAKFAST

Breakfast is an important meal.

Don't skip it and think you are saving yourself calories. Your body needs some fuel to get it going so make time to sit down and eat some fruit, cereal, toast or a yoghurt. It'll stop you feeling like a 'little something' about 10.30 – like a cup of coffee and half a packet of custard creams.

Cereal is a must – it's cheap and easy – and you should be aiming for some high fibre no-added-sugar cereal with reduced fat milk. (One modest bowl of All Bran with skimmed milk not two mammoth bowls of Sugar Puffs with silver top.) I can heartily recommend porridge, not just out of patriotic pride, but because it really does ward off hunger pangs for longer.

We should all eat more fruit – about 3 to 5 pieces a day is the government recommendation – and you should aim to get some of that in at breakfast time. As a rule, eat fruit rather than drink fruit juice. It takes longer to eat and has more fibre – save the fruit juice for when you are in a tearing hurry. You'll find recipes for quick-whizz drinks and an assortment of fruit salads over the next few pages. Somehow, fruit cut up and mixed together is more appetising and interesting than something from the fruit bowl. Make up fruit salads the night before to save time in the morning. Most of them benefit from being chilled anyway.

Toast is another good standby especially if the bread is a good dense wholemeal, thinly sliced. Spread with a scraping of my *Easy-to-spread, Reduced Fat Butter* or one of the vitamin-rich, naturally sweet fruit spreads.

Banana Malt-Shake Ⓥ

I love malt extract. We used to get a spoonful a day when we were growing up and I used to nip into the larder cupboard and sneak extra spoonfuls on the logic that if one spoonful was good for you, two spoonfuls would work wonders. Although you only use 150ml (¼pt) of milk, this drink froths up to a thick milk shake that will fill a 300ml (½pt) glass. The riper the banana, the sweeter and smoother the shake.

1 medium sized banana
150ml (¼pt) cold half-fat, vitamin-enriched milk
1 teaspoon malt extract

1 Peel the banana and break it into small pieces. Place in a liquidiser goblet. Add the milk and whizz the machine until the mixture is smooth.
2 Add the malt extract through the hole in the lid while the machine is running. Pour into a glass and drink at once.

Thick Citrus Shake Ⓥ

Whizz this up in the liquidiser for a thick, fruity milk-free shake. Add the ice-cubes if you can stand the noise. The drink separates out if it is allowed to stand so make it as you need it. This drink has all the Vitamin C you need for a day.

Makes 300ml (½pt)
2 oranges
1 small lemon
1 medium-sized banana
4 ice-cubes, optional

1 Squeeze juices from the oranges and the lemon and place in a liquidiser goblet.
2 Peel the banana, break it into small pieces and add with the ice-cubes if you are using them. Whizz until smooth. Pour into a tall glass and drink at once.

• Make today the day that you change your philosophy. Adapt this slogan – No time to eat – too busy exercising. Write it on a sheet of paper and stick it to the fridge. Make it happen.

Frothy Hot Chocolate Ⓥ

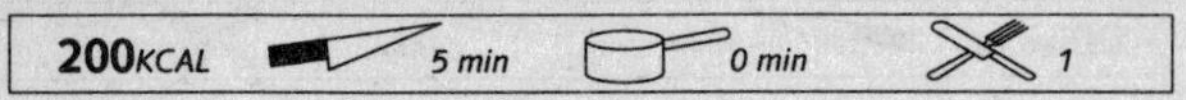

One of these shakes, and a vitamin tablet, will give you the same amount of nutrients as those expensive cans of Diet Plan Hot Chocolate mix – and is a lot cheaper. Prunes and chocolate taste wonderful together and the prunes sweeten naturally while adding valuable fibre. Please try it – you might actually like it.

250ml (½pt) half-fat, vitamin-enriched milk
2 teaspoons cocoa powder
few drops natural vanilla essence
4 canned prunes, stones taken out

1 Pour the milk into a small non stick saucepan and bring to the boil.
2 Sprinkle on the cocoa powder. Add the vanilla essence and prunes and whisk well.
3 Pour into the liquidiser goblet and run the machine for 30 seconds until mixture is frothy. Pour into a heatproof mug and drink hot.

Strawberry and Vanilla Shake Ⓥ

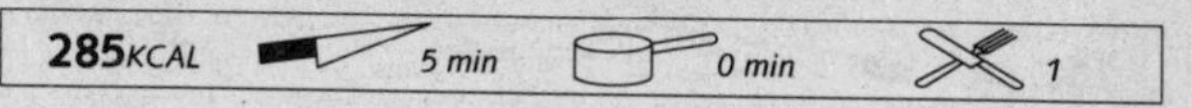

This shake is a great way to start a summer's day (or have it for a light lunch with a salad).

225g (8oz) fresh strawberries
210ml (7fl oz) half-fat, vitamin-enriched milk
50g (2oz) reduced calorie vanilla ice-cream

1 Hull the strawberries and place in a liquidiser goblet. Add the milk and whizz the machine for 30 seconds until the mixture looks smooth and pink.
2 Sieve into a measuring jug and discard the pips.
3 Return the mixture to the liquidiser goblet. Add the ice-cream and whizz the machine for a further 30 seconds.
4 Pour into a 300ml (½pt) glass and drink at once.

- If you find skimmed milk too much of a jump from full fat milk, then settle for a half-way option: half-fat milk. Here's how the calories compare.

284ml (½pt) gold top 220 calories
284ml (½pt) silver top 185 calories
284ml (½pt) half-fat 165 calories
284ml (½pt) semi-skimmed 125 calories
284ml (½pt) skimmed 100 calories

Microwave Porridge Ⓥ

Porridge is brilliant cooked in the microwave – quick, just right for one person and no messy pans to cope with. This recipe makes a porridge which has a thick consistency and which will pour slowly from the jug into your bowl. If you prefer it thinner, whisk an extra couple of spoonfuls of boiling water into the mixture at the end of the cooking time. Use a very large measuring jug because the mixture does bubble right up during cooking. You can, of course, cook it in a pan on the hob – but it will take longer and you will need to add more water to stop it sticking.

The Scots eat their porridge with salt and from a calorie point of view you should too. If you prefer it sweeter, some plump sultanas scattered on the top add more calories than a spoonful of sugar, but they add fibre too. Serve with skimmed or semi-skimmed milk.

250ml (½pt) boiling water
40g (1½oz) medium oatmeal
good pinch of salt

1 Pour the boiling water into a 1.4l (3pt) measuring jug.
2 Whisk in the oatmeal and the salt and part cover the top with cling film. Stand the jug on a

microwave-proof plate (to catch any drips).
3 Cook on full power (100%) for 2 minutes. Whisk again, part cover and cook for a further 2 minutes. Whisk again and serve.

To cook this on the hob, place all ingredients in a non-stick pan, bring to the boil and simmer, stirring continually, for 20 minutes.

Muesli Ⓥ

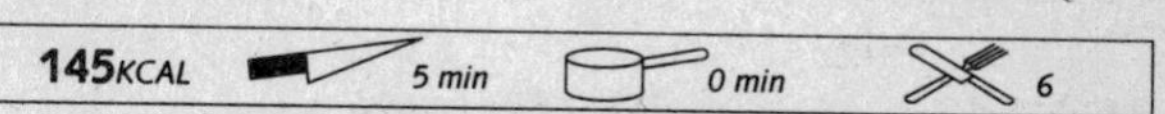

Most of us don't eat enough fibre and most women don't eat enough iron. One easy way to solve both problems is to eat All Bran. If you can't eat a whole bowl – add it to your favourite unsweetened muesli mixture. This quantity makes enough for 6 and will keep in an airtight container for up to 1 month. Serve with skimmed milk or fresh orange juice.

Makes 6 servings of 50g (1oz) each
75g (3oz) ready-to-eat dried apricots
100g (4oz) All Bran
125g (5oz) sugar-free luxury muesli

1 Cut the apricots into small pieces with a sharp knife or a pair of scissors. Place in a large bowl.
2 Add the All Bran and the muesli. Stir well to mix.
3 Weigh out 50g (2oz) and tip it into a serving bowl. Add skimmed milk or fresh orange juice.

Crunchy Granola Ⓥ

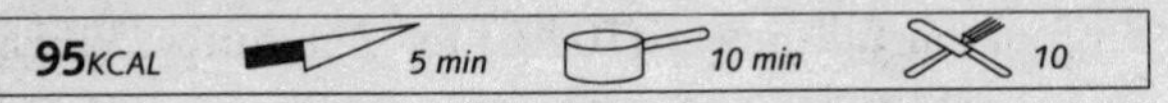

This is one of those satisfying recipes that used to require a trip to the health food shop. Nowadays you can pick everything up in a reasonable-sized supermarket. It gives a sweet, crunchy cereal that you can add to a bowl of bran flakes, stir into a yoghurt, scatter on top of puréed fruit or just nibble at when you feel like something sweet.

Makes 10 servings of 25g (1oz) each
100g (4oz) oat flakes
25g (1oz) flaked almonds
25g (1oz) sunflower seeds
50g (2oz) unsweetened bran flakes
25g (1oz) natural maple syrup
1 tablespoon sunflower oil
1 teaspoon natural vanilla essence

1 Pre-heat the oven to 150°C, 300°F, Gas 4.
2 Place the oat flakes, almonds, sunflower seeds, bran flakes, maple syrup, sunflower oil and vanilla essence together in a bowl.
3 Stir until evenly coated with oil mixture.
4 Spread in a thin layer on a baking sheet and bake in a warm oven for 5 minutes until lightly golden.
5 Stir well and cook for a further 5 minutes. Cool on the tray then store in an airtight container.

Californian Plum Spread Ⓥ

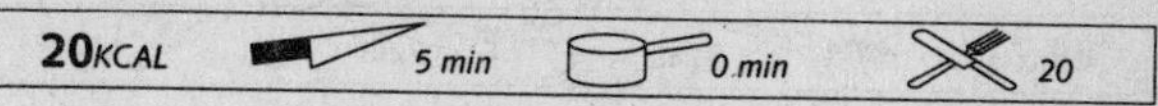

This is a super sweet spread for toast and crispbreads. It's as sweet as jam but has more fibre and vitamins and, of course, no added sugar. Spread 1 teaspoonful on toast or use it to sweeten yoghurt or stewed fruit. It'll keep in the fridge for up to 2 weeks or you can freeze it in small quantities and defrost a little at a time. (If I'd called it *Prune Spread* you'd never have read this far but that's what it is.)

100g (4oz) Californian pitted, ready-to-eat prunes
150ml (¼pt) fresh, unsweetened apple juice

1 Place the prunes and half the apple juice in a food processor. Run the machine for 1 minute until the mixture is smooth.
2 Add the rest of the apple juice and the run the machine again for another minute.
3 Spoon into a tub with a lid and store in the fridge. Spread thinly.

- Start the day with muesli, a wholewheat or bran cereal, with no sugar added. Never leave the house without eating something. Your body needs fuel to get it going. You wouldn't expect your car to run without petrol would you?

Easy-to-spread, Reduced Fat Butter

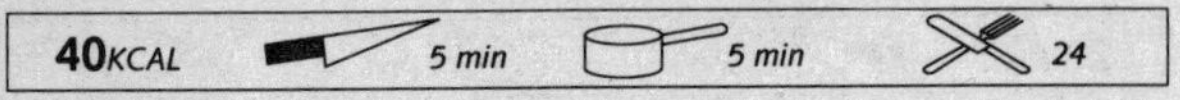

I like butter. It's pure and natural and I would rather eat it than margarine any day. Unfortunately it is, like margarine, a very concentrated source of calories and should be included in our diets sparingly. Try my reduced fat version, which will spread straight from the fridge, has the same number of calories as a low fat spread but a rich buttery flavour. It'll keep in the fridge for up to 1 week or the freezer for up to 1 month.

Makes 250g (8oz) or 24 portions.
1 sachet gelatine
125g (4oz) packet Dutch unsalted butter
150ml(¼pt) skimmed milk
4 storage tubs

1 Spoon 3 tablespoons of cold water into a heatproof mug. Shake in the sachet of gelatine and stir well. (The water will become thick and cloudy.)
2 Place the mug in a pan. Quarter fill the pan with boiling water and simmer over a medium heat until the gelatine dissolves to a clear liquid. Remove the mug and tip the water out of the pan.
3 Place the butter and the milk in the pan and heat gently, stirring until the butter melts. Do not boil. Remove the pan from the heat and stir in the liquid gelatine. Allow to cool slightly. Before the mixture

has set, whisk it lightly together with a fork to make sure that it has not separated out and divide between the clean storage tubs.

4 When set, store one portion in the door of the fridge and put the others in the freezer. Use sparingly and spread thinly.

Apricot and Orange Spread Ⓥ

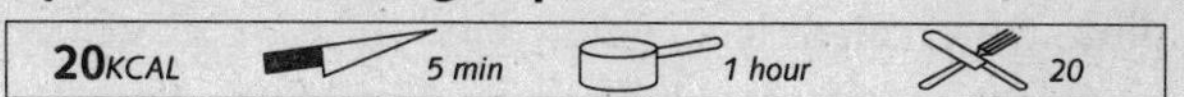

This makes a wonderful tangy spread which has the consistency of home-made lemon curd. Spread thinly on toast, stir it into natural yoghurt or unflavoured fromage frais or add spoonfuls to sweeten stewed fruit.

100g (4oz) dried apricots
125ml (¼pt) unsweetened orange juice
1 tablespoon fresh lemon juice

1 Place the apricots and orange juice in a small non-stick pan. Add 150ml (¼pt) water.

2 Bring to the boil, reduce the heat, cover and simmer for 1 hour or until the apricots are soft.

3 Place the apricots and juices in a food processor along with the lemon juice. Run the machine for 1 minute or until the mixture is thick and smooth.

4 Spoon into a tub with a lid and store in the fridge. Spread thinly.

Rhubarb with Apple and Rosehip Syrup Ⓥ

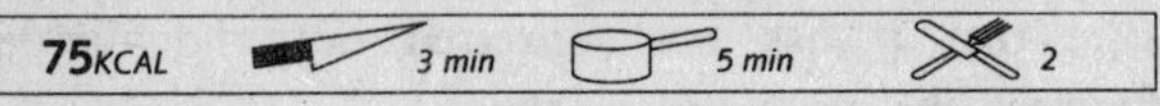

Remember rosehip syrup? I used to be given it as a child to ward off colds through the winter – it's a concentrated source of Vitamin C. You'll find it in the baby foods section of the chemist. It's a lot sweeter than sugar and adds a lovely flavour to all sorts of fruity recipes. A warmed plateful of this pink fruit salad is a good way to start a winter morning or it's nice chilled the rest of the year.

250g (8oz) small pink rhubarb stems
150ml (¼pt) fresh orange juice
2 teaspoons pure, concentrated apple and rosehip syrup

1 Rinse the rhubarb and cut into 2.5cm (1in) lengths.
2 Place in a pan with orange juice. Bring to the boil, reduce the heat, cover and simmer for 4 to 5 minutes until the rhubarb is just tender when you prod it with a knife.
3 Add the apple and rosehip syrup and stir gently to mix it in. Serve warm or cold.

- If you don't buy it, you can't eat it. Be strong at the supermarket and never shop when you are hungry.

Plums Poached with Cinnamon Ⓥ

I love those big, purpley-blue cooking plums you get in the autumn. Once cooked they turn a deep red and are wonderful, warm or cold, for breakfast or spooned into yoghurt for a pudding.

450g (1lb) cooking plums
1 cinnamon stick
1 tablespoon well-flavoured clear honey
550ml (1pt) water

1 Place the plums in a large pan. Add the cinnamon stick and the honey and cover with the water. Bring to the boil, reduce the heat and simmer gently for 20 minutes until the plums feel soft. Allow to cool.
2 Drain the juice from the plums into a measuring jug. Transfer the plums to a dish.
3 Pour the plum juice back into pan and bring to the boil. Boil for 10 minutes, without a lid on, or until the mixture has reduced and feels syrupy.
4 Pour over the plums. When cold, cover and store in the fridge for up to 3 days.

Fruits of the Forest Fromage Frais Ⓥ

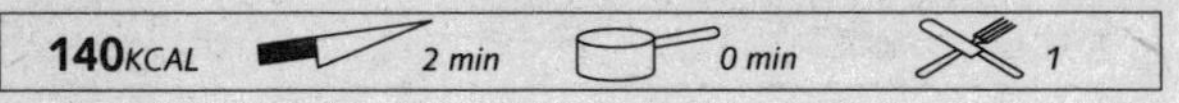

175g (6oz) frozen mixed summer berries (strawberries, raspberries, blackberries, red and blackcurrants, blueberries and cherries), defrosted
4 tablespoons 1% fat fromage frais
1 teaspoon natural maple syrup

1 Spoon the fruit into a serving bowl.
2 Mix the fromage frais with the maple syrup, spoon over the fruit and eat.

Apples with Ginger and Orange Ⓥ

Choose an apple that is naturally sweet rather than a cooking apple which needs added sugar. Serve with Greek yoghurt, flavoured with a few drops of vanilla essence or some freshly grated nutmeg.

250g (8oz) small, sweet eating apples, e.g. Cox's Orange Pippins
1 small orange
25g (1oz) stem ginger

1 Peel and core the apples. Slice into a small non-stick pan. Peel strips of rind from the orange using a canelle knife and squeeze the juice. Remove the

ginger from its syrup and finely slice.
2 Add the orange rind and juice, and the ginger to the pan. Simmer gently for 10 to 12 minutes, shaking the pan occasionally to prevent the apples from sticking. Serve hot or cold.

Pineapple and Raspberries Ⓥ

At home I call this my Friday salad because there is often nothing left worth eating in the fruit bowl. Fortunately, I always have canned pineapple in the cupboard and raspberries in the freezer. Mix them together before you go to bed and you have a lovely pinky salad in the fridge at breakfast time. (It tastes even better if you have fresh pineapple and fresh raspberries.)

100g (4oz) canned, unsweetened pineapple chunks in natural juice
100g (4oz) fresh or frozen raspberries
3 tablespoons fresh orange juice

1 Cut the pineapple chunks in half and place them in a bowl with 4 tablespoons of the juice from the can.
2 Add the raspberries and the orange juice and stir to mix.

Papaya Slices with Lime Ⓥ

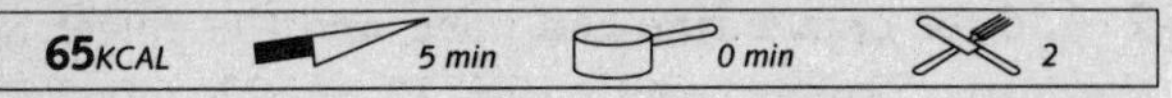

This may sound rather pretentious for breakfast but a bit of exotica and variety are good for us all. Papaya – also called pawpaw – are widely available now. They are a slightly pear-shaped fruit with mottled yellow and green skin, and inside the flesh is a vibrant coral pink with round browny-black seeds. It needs a squeeze of lime juice to bring out its flavour. Prepare it in the same way you would a melon.

1 papaya, weighing about 300g (10oz)
½ lime

1 Cut the papaya in half lengthwise and scoop out the seeds with a teaspoon.
2 Place the papaya, cut-side down, on a chopping board. Cut each half into slices and cut the skin off each slice.
3 Arrange the prepared papaya on 2 plates.
4 Squeeze the juice from the lime over the papaya slices and serve.

• Clean your teeth after every meal – it helps reduce the craving for something else. If you are still feeling nibblesome, drink a glass of water and get out of the kitchen fast.

Fresh Peach and Summer Berries Ⓥ

In the middle of summer, when it's sunny at breakfast time, treat yourself to this. Served as a fruit salad with a vanilla fromage frais, or stirred into yoghurt, it's a fresh, light way to start the day.

1 fresh ripe peach
50g (2oz) small strawberries
50g (2oz) raspberries
ground black pepper

1 To skin the peach: place it in a small bowl and cover it with boiling water. Leave for 20 seconds and then drain. Mark a cross at the stalk end and peel the skin off in four pieces.
2 Cut the peach in half and twist the two halves in opposite directions to separate them. Remove the flat oval stone with a teaspoon. Place the peach, cut-side down, on a plate and slice thinly.
3 Hull the strawberries and halve.
4 Mix the peach slices, strawberries and raspberries together in a bowl and sprinkle with ground black pepper.

Hot Orange and Grapefruit Ⓥ

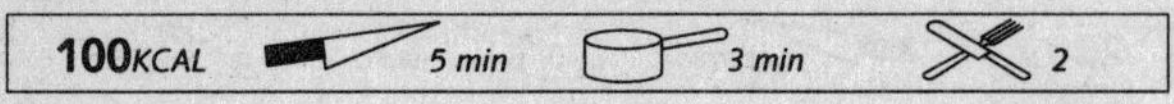

If you are used to dieting, you might remember the Mayo Clinic diet. I went on it once when I was a student and all I can remember now is that it involved eating large amounts of grapefruit halves and boiled eggs. The two foods for me now sum up all that is bad about fad diets and are inextricably linked with hunger. Grapefruit cut into segments I can enjoy, though, and I buy the naturally sweet ruby grapefruits when they are in season.

1 grapefruit
2 oranges
5 tablespoons unsweetened pineapple juice

1 Cut the skin and white pith off the grapefruit and the oranges using a sharp knife. Hold the grapefruit over a small saucepan. Cut between the white membranes to cut out the grapefruit segments and let them drop into the pan.
2 When all the segments are cut, squeeze the juice from the membranes into the pan and then throw these away. Repeat the process with the oranges.
3 Add the pineapple juice. Bring the mixture slowly to the boil to warm the segments through. Serve hot.

Mixed Melon with Black Grapes Ⓥ

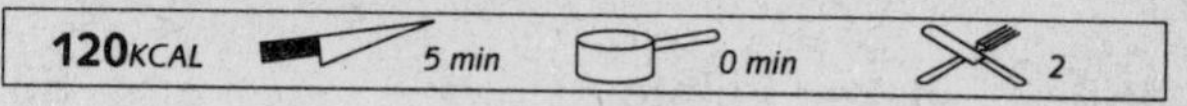

This is a really refreshing salad, naturally sweet and much more exciting somehow than a wedge of melon and a bunch of grapes eaten separately. Vary the melons depending on what's ripe when you go shopping – the calories are all much the same whatever the variety. Watermelon, with its bright pink flesh and flat black seeds is also refreshing when in season. Anything you can't eat at breakfast would make a good after-dinner pud at night, or travels well in a tub for a packed lunch or a picnic.

¼ honeydew melon
½ small Galia melon
75g (3oz) seedless black grapes

1 Scrape the seeds out of the centres of the melons using a teaspoon. Cut into slices and then cut the flesh off the skin and cut into small chunks.
2 Pull the grapes off their stalks and cut in half. Mix the melon and grapes in a serving bowl. Chill, if there's time.

• Don't let your weight rule your life. For most of us it is not a matter of life and death. Try to think less about food and more about exercise.

BAKED POTATOES

Handy Measures
175g (6oz) potato is 150 calories
200g (7oz) potato is 175 calories
225g (8oz) potato is 200 calories
250g (9oz) potato is 225 calories
280g (10oz) potato is 250 calories
Every extra ounce adds an extra 25 calories

BAKED POTATOES

A quick meal, ideal for one.

A baked potato with a tasty filling and some extra vegetables makes a satisfying lunch or supper. In a microwave oven, a potato will cook in around 5 minutes which makes it very practical for a quick meal, ideal for one person and gives you enough time to get together a really lovely salad to enjoy with it. A small baked potato will cook in 35 to 45 minutes in a traditional oven on a high setting which, with a bit of planning, isn't unreasonably long to wait. (Don't hang around the kitchen while it is cooking – you have time to pedal the exercise bike, water the garden or soak in a hot soapy bath.)

Choose a potato that bakes well. There are lots of different varieties and what's on sale near you will depend on where you live and the time of year. I find potatoes like Estima and Cara are especially good for baking. If you are buying in a supermarket check the shelf label or the bag for information, otherwise ask your greengrocer. All potatoes are not the same. Buy them loose if you can and choose them with care. The size will depend on how hungry you are and how many calories you want to eat (see chart opposite). Weigh them so you get the feel of the size you need and only buy what you will use in the next few days. Potatoes are best eaten fresh and they do seem to go green and sprout faster than they used to, so use them up quickly.

All the fillings (see the recipes that follow) were tested in 175g (6oz) baked potatoes. If you cook a larger one, remember to add on the extra calories. Remember to eat the skin too – it's a useful source of fibre and most of the vitamins are stored just under the skin.

Baked Potato Ⓥ

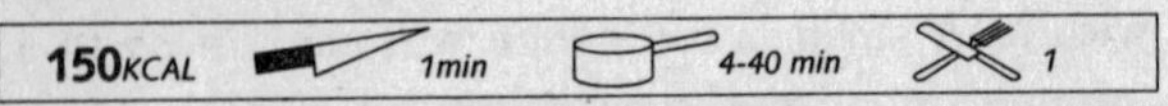

A baked potato with a tasty filling and some extra vegetables or salad makes a satisfying lunch or supper. First choose your potato with the help of the chart on page 86. The size will depend on how hungry you are and how many calories you want to eat.

Baked potatoes are really so easy – the hard part is choosing a filling.

175g (6oz) good baking potato

To microwave

1 Scrub the potato and prick it a couple of times with a fork. Place in a piece of kitchen paper on the microwave turntable and cook on full power (100%) for 4 minutes. Prod with a fork. If the potato feels hard, put it in for another minute and then prod it again. If it feels soft it's ready. If the skin is very wrinkled, you've overdone it – the potato will be fine to eat but make a note to give a potato of that size a minute less next time.

To cook conventionally

1 Pre-heat oven to its highest setting and place a baked potato directly on the oven shelf. Bake for 35 to 40 minutes or until the potato feels soft all the way through when you prod it with a fork.

Greek Yoghurt and Pesto Potato Ⓥ

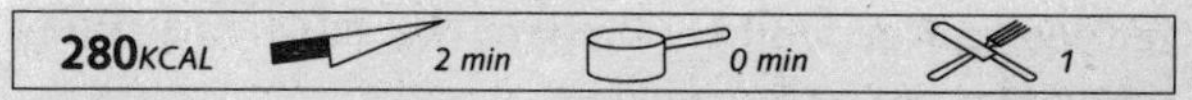

This is a real store-cupboard standby but delicious nonetheless. Use pesto in a jar or, better still, a spoonful of fresh pesto sauce. Serve with a fresh tomato salad scattered with torn basil leaves.

3 tablespoons Greek yoghurt
1 tablespoon fresh pesto
hot baked potato (see recipe on page 88)

1 Spoon the yoghurt and the pesto into a small bowl and stir well to mix.
2 Halve the potato and open out flat. Scoop some of the potato out of its skin and mash with a fork. Add the yoghurt mixture, mash together and pile the mixture back into the potato skin. Serve hot.

Prawn Cocktail Potato

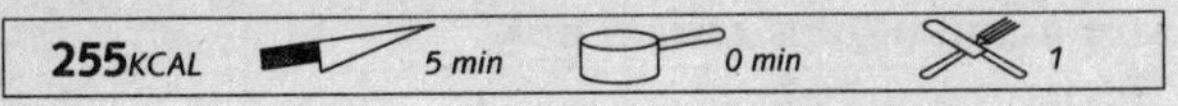

Since you will eat only a tiny amount of prawns, treat yourself to good ones. Pass by the bargain bags of shrimp-like, water-soaked ones with freezer burn in the supermarket and choose some plump tiger prawns or some large peeled prawns fresh from Scottish waters via the fishmonger or the fresh fish counter. Make this a baked potato to remember. Serve with chopped fresh tomatoes and shredded lettuce and cucumber. Prepare the salad and filling while the potato is cooking.

50g (2oz) cooked peeled prawns
1 tablespoon reduced calorie mayonnaise
1 teaspoon Greek yoghurt
1 teaspoon tomato ketchup
squeeze of fresh lemon juice
Worcestershire sauce
ground black pepper
hot baked potato (see recipe on page 88)

1 Rinse and pat dry the prawns.
2 Make the sauce: put the mayonnaise, yoghurt, tomato ketchup, lemon juice and a dash of Worcestershire sauce in a small bowl. Add some pepper, mix well. Stir in the prawns.
3 Halve the potato and open flat. Pile the prawn mixture on top. Serve straight away.

Curried Beans Potato Ⓥ

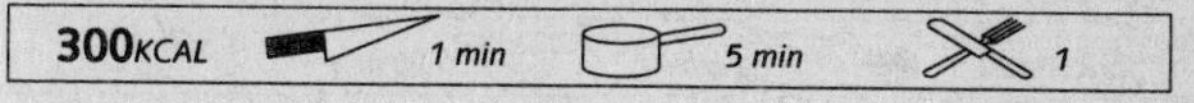

Baked beans are a wonderful food. Cheap, easy and good for you. Full of flavour and fibre, they make a moist filling for a tattie.

1 small onion
1 teaspoon oil
1 teaspoon garam masala (curry spices)
175g (6oz) reduced sugar baked beans and some of their juice
hot baked potato (see recipe on page 88)

1 Peel and finely chop the onion. Heat the oil in a small non-stick frying pan and fry the onion over a medium heat for 2 to 3 minutes until softened but not browned.
2 Add the garam masala and stir well. Cook for a further 30 seconds, stirring all the time.
3 Add the beans and bring to the boil, stirring.
4 Halve the potato and open out flat. Pour the beans over the top. Serve straight away.

Kipper and Horseradish Potato

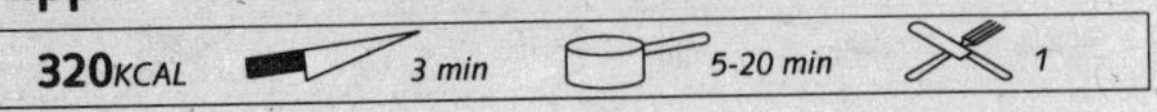

Strongly flavoured foods are very satisfying when you are cutting back on quantity. Boil-in-the-bag fillets of kippers mean no smell and no bones, just moist, well-flavoured fish. As most of them come with butter though, be strong willed and discard the cooking juices.

50g (2oz) boil-in-the-bag, boneless, skinless kipper fillet
hot baked potato (see recipe on page 88)
1 teaspoon creamed horseradish sauce
1 tablespoon reduced calorie mayonnaise
black pepper to taste
squeeze of fresh lemon juice

1 Cook the kipper fillets according to the instructions on the pack – usually by simmering in a pan of water or by cooking in the microwave oven. Slit the bag, drain and transfer the contents to a large plate. Weigh out 50g (2oz), skin if necessary and mash with a fork.
2 Halve the potato and open out flat. Scoop most of the potato out of the skin and add to the kipper. Add the horseradish, mayonnaise, black pepper and a squeeze of lemon juice. Mash well.
3 Pile it all back into the potato skins. Serve straight away.

Salmon, Cucumber and Chive Potato

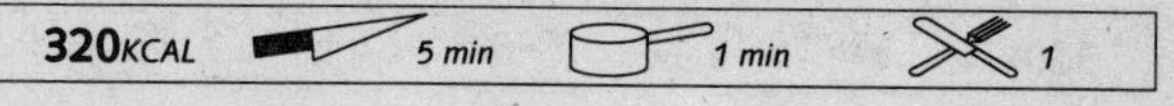

2.5cm (1in) piece cucumber
50g (2oz) canned red salmon
2 tablespoons reduced calorie mayonnaise
1 teaspoon chopped fresh chives
ground black pepper
hot baked potato (see recipe on page 88)

1 Peel the skin from the cucumber. Slice the cucumber and then cut into small dice.
2 Drain the salmon, remove the skin and any central bone and mash the salmon well.
3 Add the cucumber, mayonnaise, chives and black pepper and mix lightly together.
4 Halve the potato and open out flat. Scoop some of the potato out and mash with a fork. Mix in the salmon.
5 Pile the mixture back into the potato skins. Serve straight away.

• Sometimes, when you think you need food, your body is really needing liquid. Have a glass of water or a diet drink and see if the feeling goes away.

Mature Cheese and Mango Chutney Potato Ⓥ

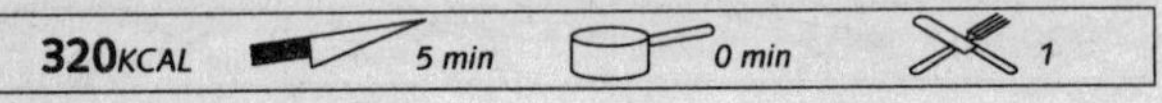

This filling has as many variations as there are cheeses and chutneys. A mature, or an extra-mature, cheese has a stronger flavour so you need to eat less. It's slightly pricier, but I think it's worth the extra cost.

2 tablespoons Greek yoghurt
2 teaspoons mango and ginger chutney
25g (1oz) mature Cheddar cheese
40g (1½oz) carrot
hot baked potato (see recipe on page 88)

1 Place the yoghurt and chutney in a small bowl and mix together.
2 Grate the cheese and the carrot on a large plate and mix together. Tip into the yoghurt mixture and stir to mix.
3 Halve the potato and open out. Pile the mixture on top. Serve straight away.

• An exercise bike is only doing you good if you sit on it and make the pedals go round!

Coronation Chicken Potato

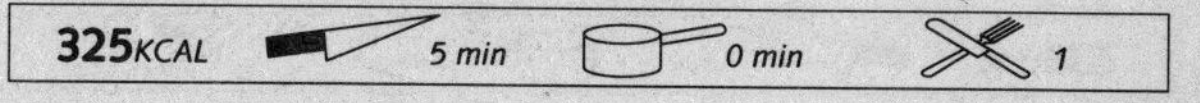

Coronation chicken was created for the Queen's coronation and has become a classic. Originally a rich mixture of cream, curry and apricots, this quick-mix version is full of flavour but has a more restrained calorie count.

1 tablespoon reduced sugar peach jam
½ teaspoon mild curry paste
2 tablespoons Greek yoghurt
50g (2oz) cooked chicken breast
hot baked potato (see recipe on page 88)

1 Spoon the jam, curry paste and yoghurt into a small bowl and stir well to mix.
2 Finely dice the chicken and stir into the sauce.
3 Halve the baked potato and open out flat. Fill with the chicken mixture. Serve straight away.

- Exercise will
  - Allow you let off steam and feel less stressed
  - Help you sleep well
  - Make you feel better about yourself
  - Give you more energy.

Tuna and Celery Potato

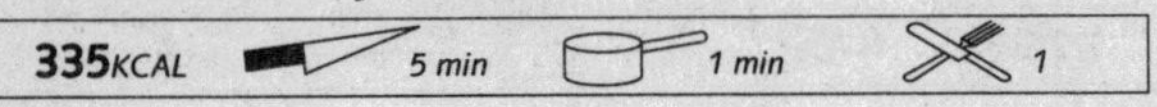

I am not a great celery lover but I do like it in this filling because it adds a bit of crunch.

50g (2oz) canned tuna
½ stick of celery
1 tablespoon fresh chopped parsley
1 tablespoon tartare sauce
1 tablespoon reduced calorie mayonnaise
hot baked potato (see recipe on page 88)

1 Drain the tuna into a sieve and rinse with cold water.
2 Finely chop the celery. Put the tuna, celery and parsley into a bowl. Spoon in the tartare sauce and the mayonnaise and stir well to mix.
3 Halve the potato and open out flat. Scoop most of the potato out of the skin and mash. Add the tuna mixture and mix well.
4 Pile back into the skins. Serve straight away.

• Be realistic. Make gradual but lasting changes. Do the easy things first and take your time. You want the weight loss to last, who cares how long it takes? Make small manageable changes to your diet. Even if you lost 2lbs (1kg) a month, this time next year, you could weigh a lot less.

Blue Cheese and Tomato Potato Ⓥ

Look out for Danish Blue cheese sold, wrapped in foil, in tiny squares. You can sometimes get it at the pick-and-mix cheese section in larger supermarkets or it comes in a box of 6 small wrapped cubes. Handy portion control.

50g (2oz) Danish blue cheese
1 ripe plum tomato
hot baked potato (see recipe on page 88)

1 Finely dice the cheese and the tomatoes.
2 Halve the potato and open flat. Scoop some of the potato out of its skin and mash with a fork. Add the cheese and tomato mixture and stir well.
3 Pile the mixture back into the potato skins. Serve straight away.

• Do you hardly eat a thing and still not lose weight? Most people don't have a really accurate picture of what they eat. Write down everything you put in your mouth as you go along. Look it up in the calorie charts and tot up the calories. A food diary of when, what and where you eat often highlights the times that you eat when you are not really hungry. Many would-be dieters eat much more than they think they are eating.

SANDWICHES

Adopt the Scandinavian habit of open sandwiches.

Why settle for spongy, white, processed bread when, for the same calories, you could be eating a slice of a French farmhouse loaf or something crusty and Italian? There has never been such a good range to choose from and bread now comes with lots of built-in flavours – studded with walnuts or extra grains and seeds, speckled with herbs, olives, onions or sun-dried tomatoes. Perhaps surprisingly, the calories don't differ much – even for Ciabatta, a flat Italian, crusty, open-textured white bread made with extra virgin olive oil. It is now stocked by all the big supermarkets and because they are sparing with the olive oil, you can enjoy a 2.5cm (1in) slice for only 95 calories.

Treat yourself to good bread. Buy a flavoursome loaf from a good baker and get them to slice it thinly for you. Freeze it when you get home in 2-slice portions. Then you'll always have good sandwich material to hand and this will avoid any temptation to eat more than your allotted portion.

From a calorie point of view there is not much difference between white and wholemeal bread, but from a healthy eating standpoint choose wholemeal every time. Wholemeal is more satisfying as it is made from flour that has all the fibre from the wheat still in it and so it will keep hunger away for longer. If you don't like that dense, moist texture you get with a proper organic, stone-ground wholemeal, choose one of the lighter 'brown' breads with oat bran, oatmeal or multi-grains in them.

It's a good idea to adopt the Scandinavian habit of open sandwiches. Not only do you the save the 70 or so calories that the top slice of bread would have added but you get to see the filling so the sandwich looks more appealing. Try thinking of sandwiches as knife and fork food – arrange a colourful salad on the plate, slice some good bread, add a topping, sit down and make a meal of it.

Smoked Ham and Curried Banana

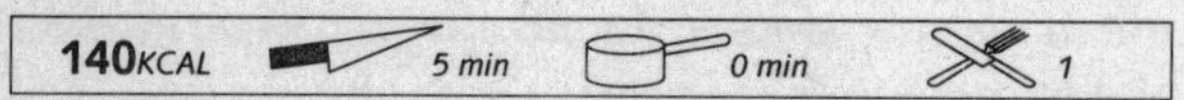

This is a great filling – sweet, sour and salty all at once. Make it just before you want to eat it.

50g (2oz) banana, weighed after peeling
½ teaspoon mild lime pickle
1 small slice wholemeal bread weighing 25g (1oz)
8 watercress leaves, minus stalks
25g (1oz) lean smoked ham

1 Mash the banana in a small bowl with a fork. Add the lime pickle and mash into the banana.
2 Spread over the bread. Top with the watercress.
3 Slice the ham into strips and scatter over the top.

Hot Egg and Cress Ⓥ

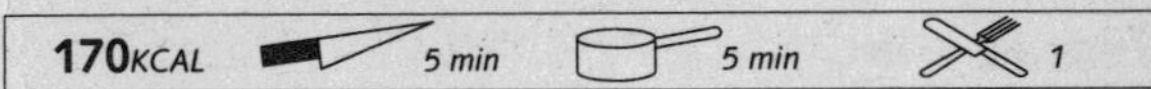

I have a weakness for a good egg sandwich. Free range eggs make me feel better, even when I'm sure I can't tell the difference in flavour between it and its badly treated battery cousin. (Caloriewise they are the same). Mustard and cress is a mix of two sorts of seed and has a peppery flavour; salad cress is the milder sort. Add some splendid brown bread, some freshly ground pepper and enjoy.

1 free range egg, size 3
2 teaspoons reduced fat mayonnaise
ground black pepper
1 thin slice wholemeal bread weighing 25g (1oz)
⅓ box mustard and cress or salad cress

1 Put the egg in a small pan, cover with cold water and bring to the boil. As soon as it starts to boil, set the timer to 5 minutes. Reduce the heat and simmer for 5 minutes exactly, lift out of the pan with a slotted spoon and rinse under cold water.
2 Tap the rounded ends of the egg on the work surface to break the shell. Peel and put, still warm, into a small bowl. Mash with a fork.
3 Add mayonnaise and pepper and stir to mix.
4 Spread the mixture onto the slice of bread. Snip mustard and cress off with scissors and layer over the egg. Eat while still warm.

Feta, Olive, Tomato and Thyme Ⓥ

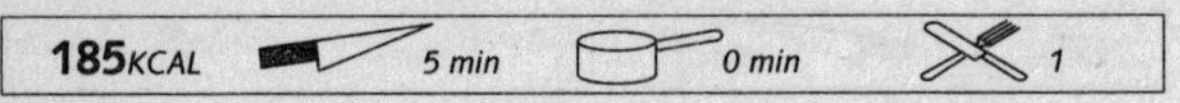

I love this Greek cheese and tomato sandwich. Feta is salty and full of flavour and so are Greek kalamati olives. Choose tomatoes that have been ripened in the sun (or supermarket varieties that have been grown for flavour). Thyme is one of those wonderful all-year-round herbs that you seem to be able to plant and forget and still it keeps on growing. Buy a pot from the garden centre and keep it on the windowsill. Serve with a salad of Cos lettuce and cucumber.

25g (1oz) feta cheese
3 black olives
4 cherry tomatoes
1 slice crusty white bread weighing 25g (1oz)
few sprigs fresh thyme
ground black pepper

1 Drain the feta, put it on a plate and mash with a fork. Slit the olives with a knife, take out the stone and halve the olives. Halve the tomatoes.
2 Spread the slice of bread with the feta. Top with the olives and tomatoes. Scatter leaves of fresh thyme over and sprinkle with pepper.

Tuna with Horseradish and Cucumber

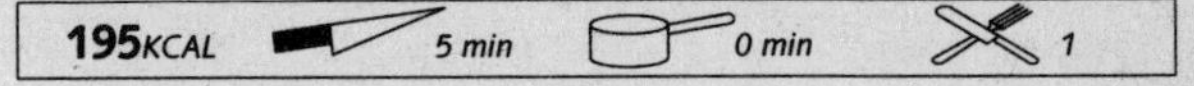

From a calorie point of view, tuna in spring water or tuna in brine are the best choice, but I do find them rather dry. For flavour, I buy tuna in oil and rinse it in a sieve under the cold tap before I use it. That way you get a moister fish with the extra calories washed away.

50g (2oz) canned tuna
1 teaspoon reduced fat mayonnaise
1 teaspoon Greek yoghurt
1 teaspoon creamed horseradish sauce
2.5cm (1in) cucumber
1 ripe tomato
1 thin slice oatmeal bread weighing 25g (1oz)

1 Drain the tuna into a sieve and rinse.
2 Spoon the mayonnaise, yoghurt and horseradish into a bowl and stir to mix. Add the tuna and stir to coat.
3 Thinly slice the cucumber and the tomato. Arrange the cucumber on the bread, top with the tuna mixture and cover with the tomatoes.

- If you must buy mass produced white bread, choose the sort that has extra grains added, so at least you get a little goodness from it.

Chicken with Mustard and Dill

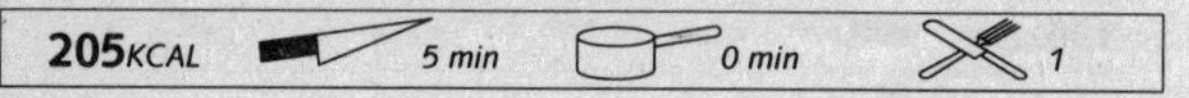

This is a really great sandwich. I stumbled across the idea when I was trying out a recipe for a mustard and dill sauce to go with Gravadlax. The same flavours mixed with mayonnaise work superbly together.

50g (2oz) roast, boneless, skinless chicken breast
1 tablespoon reduced fat mayonnaise
½ teaspoon Dijon mustard
½ teaspoon well-flavoured clear honey
1 tablespoon chopped fresh dill
1 slice of iceberg lettuce
1 thin slice oatmeal bread weighing 25g (1oz)
ground black pepper

1 Thinly slice the chicken.
2 Spoon the mayonnaise, mustard and honey into a mixing bowl. Add the dill and stir to mix.
3 Add the chicken and stir well until all the chicken is coated.
4 Arrange the lettuce on the bread. Pile the chicken mixture on top and smooth it flat. Season with pepper.

Mozzarella, Tomato and Basil Ⓥ

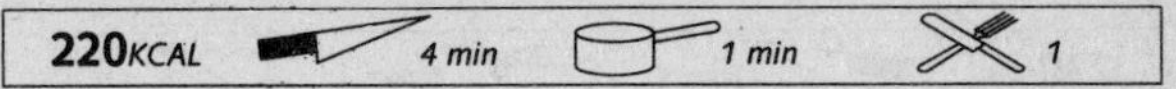

This sandwich is good cold and great grilled and served warm. If you have any, spread the bread with a teaspoon of the *Black Olive Paste* (see recipe on page 161) and remember to add the calories.

1 ripe plum tomato
40g (1½oz) mozzarella
several fresh basil leaves
1 slice olive bread or Ciabatta weighing 25g (1oz)
ground black pepper

1 Thinly slice the tomato and the mozzarella.
2 Arrange the basil leaves on the bread. Overlap the slices of tomatoes and mozzarella on top and sprinkle with black pepper.
3 Serve cold or pop under a medium grill for 1 minute until the mozzarella melts.

- If you are used to buying ready-sliced pre-packaged bread for sandwiches, then trade down a size to save calories without appearing to eat less. If you normally use 2 slices of thick-cut (180 calories), use 2 slices of medium-cut instead and you'll save 30 calories without really trying. Trade down from thick-cut to thin-cut bread and you'll save 60 calories.

Prawn Cocktail with Watercress

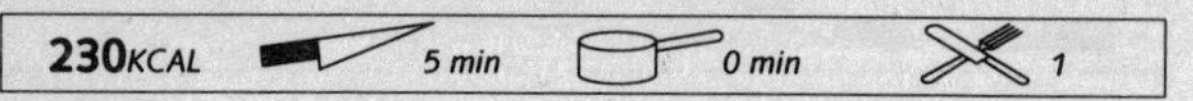

You get a lot of prawns for your calories and they are wonderful in a sandwich. Buy fresh if you can. If you are using frozen, allow them to defrost slowly in the fridge and pat them dry before using. Serve with a fresh tomato salad.

2 teaspoons reduced fat mayonnaise
1 teaspoon tomato ketchup
Worcestershire sauce
squeeze lemon juice
ground black pepper
75g (3oz) cooked, peeled prawns
3 leaves from a little gem lettuce
9 watercress leaves, minus stalks
1 thin slice oatmeal bread weighing 25g (1oz)

1 Spoon the mayonnaise, tomato ketchup, a good dash of Worcestershire sauce, lemon juice and black pepper into a small bowl and stir to mix.
2 Add the prawns and stir to coat.
3 Place the lettuce leaves on the bread, cover with most of the watercress leaves and spoon on the prawns and their sauce.
4 Top with the reserved watercress leaves.

Pickled Herring and Cream Cheese

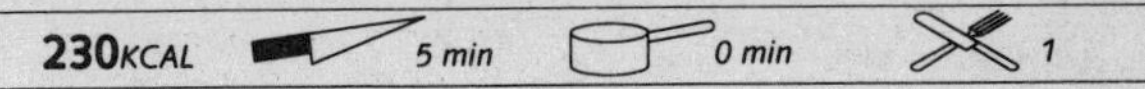

Sweet pickled herrings, sold in plastic tubs or in jars with a sweet vinegar and often gherkins or onions rings for flavouring, make a great continental-style open sandwich. They come as flat fillets or roll-mops – fillets of herring rolled and secured with a small flat wooden stick – and keep well in the fridge. Herring is one of the 'good-for-you' fish, rich in the sort of oils that doctors recommend for healthy hearts. You should try to eat fish like this at least once a week. I serve this sandwich with a plain green salad and some sliced pickled beetroot.

2.5cm (1in) piece of fresh cucumber
40g (1½oz) pumpernickel
25g (1oz) smooth reduced fat soft cheese
25g (1oz) pickled herring, weighed when drained
1 teaspoon chopped fresh dill

1 Cut the cucumber into 4 or 5 slices. Arrange the pumpernickel on a serving plate. Spread with the soft cheese. Top with the cucumber.
2 Cut the herring into bite-size pieces and arrange over the cucumber. Scatter the dill over and serve.

Cheese, Carrot and Sultana Ⓥ

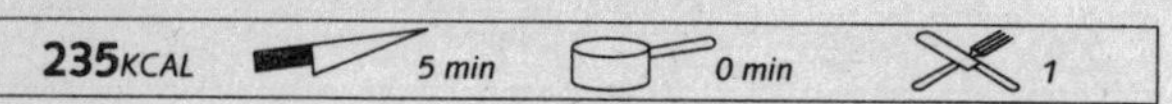

Choose a mature or an extra-mature Cheddar with bags of flavour, mix it half and half with something low calorie, like carrot, and the sultanas will add some natural sweetness. Serve with some soft, round lettuce leaves and a pickled onion and you have a sort of calorie-counted ploughman's lunch. This filling is good served lightly grilled or warmed through in the microwave oven.

25g (1oz) mature Cheddar cheese
40g (1½oz) carrot
15g (½oz) sultanas
1 teaspoon chutney
1 thin slice Granary bread weighing 25g (1oz)

1 Coarsely grate the Cheddar and the carrot onto a plate. Add the sultanas and chutney and mix together.
2 Pile the mixture onto one slice of bread and spread to the edges. (The mixture will seem quite dry, but is moist to eat.)

Tandoori Chicken with Iceberg and Mint

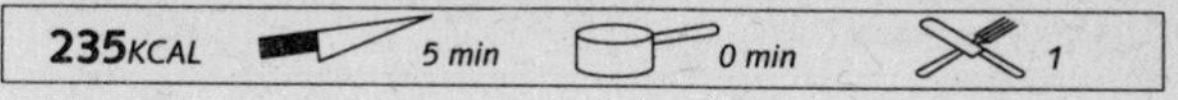

A chicken salad sandwich with a difference. Bought ready-tandooried chicken is great with yoghurt and mint. Serve with a salad of cucumber and spring onions or a few finely chopped red chillies. If you are feeling fanciful, you could garnish with a sprig of fresh mint.

1 small slice dense wholemeal bread weighing 25g (1oz)
1 tablespoon Greek yoghurt
3 fresh mint leaves
1 thin slice of iceberg lettuce
50g (2oz) cooked tandoori chicken breast fillet

1 Arrange the bread on a serving plate. Spread the yoghurt over the bread. Finely shred the mint leaves and scatter over the yoghurt.
2 Arrange the lettuce on top. Thinly slice the chicken and arrange over the lettuce.

- Don't butter both slices of bread when making sandwiches.
- Never use butter straight from the fridge. When it's hard you spread on twice as much.
- If your sandwich filling is moist, don't use any butter or margarine on the bread.

Chicken Salad with Curried Mango Mayo

Chicken can be dry, especially if it has been roasted, so it needs a good dressing. This dressing is sweet and slightly spicy.

1 tablespoon reduced fat mayonnaise
2 teaspoons mango chutney
1 teaspoon curry paste
3 leaves from a round lettuce
50g (2oz) roast, boneless, skinless chicken breast
1 thin slice wholemeal bread weighing 25g (1oz)

1 Spoon the mayonnaise, chutney and curry paste into a bowl and stir together.
2 Rinse the lettuce and shake dry. Thinly slice the chicken.
3 Spread half the mayonnaise mixture over the bread, top with the lettuce and the sliced chicken. Cover with the remaining mayonnaise mixture.

- If you can't get used to eating open wholemeal sandwiches, with just one slice of bread, try this halfway house. Wholemeal on the bottom, white on the top. Looks like a white bread sandwich but is better for you than all white. (I find this goes down well with children and grown men!)

Smooth Cheese, Dates and Walnuts Ⓥ

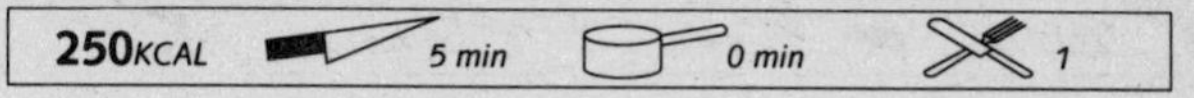

Who says sandwiches have to be savoury? I love this sandwich on dense wholemeal bread from the health food shop. Look out for fresh Medjool dates which are as natural as they come and are sweet and sticky. (The ones that come in long rounded-ended boxes are often sprayed with glucose syrup so should be washed before you eat them to rinse off unnecessary calories.) Next time you buy a packet of walnuts, toast them under the grill when you next have it on, cool and store in a jar with a tight-fitting lid. Toasting brings out their flavour.

3 plump fresh dates
3 walnut halves, toasted if possible
25g (1oz) smooth, reduced fat soft cheese
1 small slice wholemeal bread weighing 25g (1oz)

1 Slit the dates and remove the stone. Cut the dates in half. Halve the walnuts.
2 Spread the cheese over the bread. Top with the dates and walnuts.

Smoked Turkey with Coleslaw

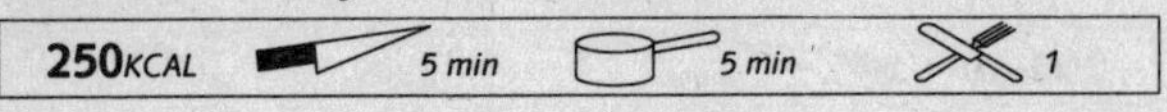

You need a good dense bread to cope with a coleslaw filling. A rye or an organic, stoneground loaf is ideal but slice it thinly. Smoked turkey sounds rather grand but it has more flavour than just plain old turkey and comes in slices, pre-packed, in the supermarket. Look out for ready-shredded cabbage mixed with carrot and sold as coleslaw mix in the vegetables section of the supermarket. It is often more economical than buying a whole cabbage and some carrots.

1 teaspoon reduced fat mayonnaise
1 teaspoon thick Greek yoghurt
1 teaspoon Dijon mustard
50g (2oz) coleslaw mix (half hard white cabbage and half carrot, finely shredded)
2 slices smoked turkey weighing 40g (1½oz) together
1 thin slice rye or wholemeal bread
1 teaspoon chopped fresh parsley

1 Spoon the mayonnaise, yoghurt and mustard into a large bowl. Add the prepared shredded vegetables and stir to mix.
2 Place the turkey on the bread and top with the coleslaw. Sprinkle on the parsley.

Pumpernickel with Edam and Gherkins Ⓥ

Pumpernickel is one of those dark, dense, grainy breads which is great to use for open sandwiches. Buy it ready sliced in pre-packed and re-sealable containers and it keeps well for ages. A great store-cupboard standby. Look out for Edam with black peppercorns or caraway seeds in it. Both have similar calories but bags more taste than the traditional plain version.

50g (2oz) Edam cheese with black peppercorns
1 small pickled gherkin
2 leaves from a round lettuce
1 slice pumpernickel bread weighing 40g (1½oz)

1 Coarsely grate the Edam and thinly slice the gherkin.
2 Arrange the lettuce on the pumpernickel and pile the Edam and gherkins on top.

• From a calorie point of view, ready-sliced bread is always the same size, thickness and weight and is a better bet than a loaf you slice yourself. It's easy to double the calories in a slice by not slicing thinly enough.

Smoked Salmon with Lime and Black Pepper

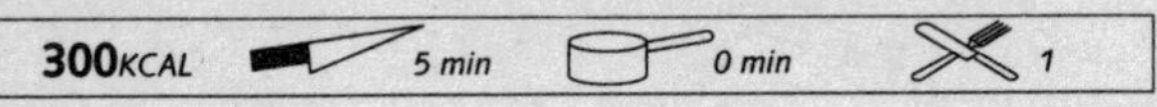

Smoked salmon (or smoked trout) seems a very extravagant sandwich filling but, made at home, they still work out cheaper than buying a sandwich with a much more ordinary inside. Because you are eating less, you should be spending less on food, so you can afford little luxuries now and then. Besides, we all have birthdays.

¼ small lime
25g (1oz) smooth, low fat soft cheese
ground black pepper
1 thin slice wholemeal bread weighing 25g (1oz)
40g (1½oz) smoked salmon or smoked trout
2.5cm (1in) piece cucumber

1 Finely grate the rind from the lime and squeeze the juice into a small bowl.
2 Add the soft cheese and a good grinding of black pepper and beat until light and creamy.
3 Spread the bread with the cheese mixture. Top with slices of salmon or trout.
4 Thinly slice the cucumber and arrange over the top. Sprinkle lightly with more black pepper.

Spinach and Gorgonzola with Walnuts Ⓥ

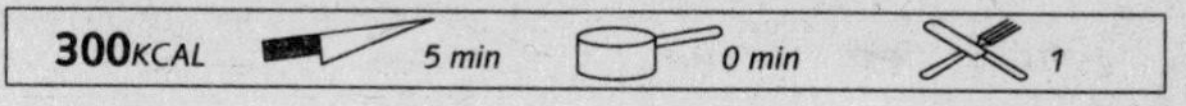

Gorgonzola is one of my favourite cheeses. It is well-flavoured, pungently blue, yet creamy and makes a really delicious sandwich.

40g (1½oz) Gorgonzola cheese
5 fresh young spinach leaves
1 slice of crusty French pain de campagne or other well-flavoured white bread weighing 40g (1½oz)
1 teaspoon walnut pieces

1 Place the Gorgonzola in a small bowl and beat well until creamy.
2 Arrange the spinach leaves on the bread.
3 Spread the cheese mixture onto the leaves and scatter the walnut pieces over the top.

• It's not the bread but the spread that piles on the calories. As an alternative to butter or margarine try:
- a very low fat spread
- 1 teaspoon of reduced fat mayonnaise
- 1 teaspoon of the *Easy-to-spread Reduced Fat Butter* (see recipe on page 78), *Black Olive Paste* (see recipe on page 161), *Roast Garlic Paste* (see recipe on page 118) or *Garlic and Chilli Paste* (see recipe on page 119)

Camembert with Black Grapes Ⓥ

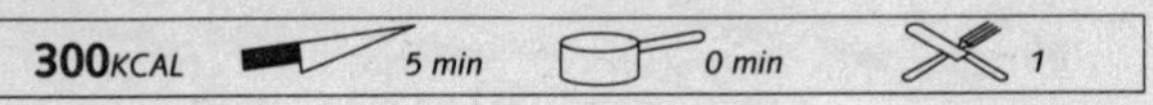

Unpasteurised Camembert ripens to a much fuller flavour and softer texture than the chalky pasteurised stuff that comes pre-packed. I buy it when the inside is runny and it smells ripe enough to smell it through any packaging it may be wrapped in. If you can find it, buy it - the calories are the same. This sandwich is great on a crusty French stick or a wholemeal baguette. Serve with a salad of mixed leaves from one of those pre-packed bags in the supermarket.

50g (2oz) baguette
50g (2oz) ripe Camembert
5 large, seedless black grapes

1 Slice lengthwise and scoop out the insides of the baguette. Give this to the birds. Slice the Camembert and halve the grapes.
2 Spread the Camembert over the bread and top with the grapes. Fold the baguette over. Serve at room temperature.

• If you are going to be successful in keeping your weight under control forever, you have to eat low fat, low sugar, high fibre foods, most of the time, for the rest of your life. You can do it.

Bacon, Lettuce and Tomato

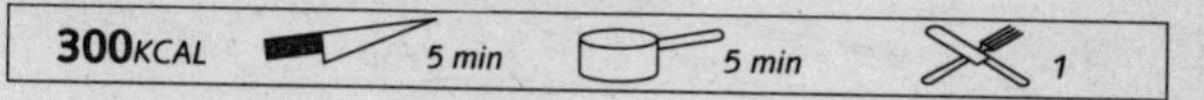

This is a classic combination, a BLT – in sandwich bar speak. Buy the best, leanest, home-cured (British) smoked bacon you can find. Trim off any excess fat and give it to the birds. You don't need the calories and it'll only set your grill pan on fire.

2 rashers lean, smoked, back bacon weighing 50g (2oz)
1 large ripe tomato
2 thin slices toast weighing 50g (2oz)
1 teaspoon reduced fat mayonnaise
1 thick slice of iceberg lettuce
wedge of fresh lemon

1 Pre-heat the grill to its highest setting. Trim all the fat from the bacon and grill it lightly for 1½ minutes on each side or until cooked through.
2 Thinly slice the tomato.
3 Spread 1 slice of toast with the mayonnaise, top with the lettuce and the tomato and squeeze over some juice from the lemon wedge.
4 Top with the bacon and the second slice of toast, and press the sandwich down firmly. Cut in half and eat straight away or later.

Roast Garlic Paste Ⓥ

When roasted, garlic becomes sweet and sticky and makes a great paste to spread on bread instead of butter or margarine. I usually roast a garlic bulb when I have the oven on for something else. This paste keeps for up to 1 month.

1 bulb (about 20 cloves) of garlic

1 Pre-heat oven to 200°C, 400°F, Gas 6.
2 Put the garlic bulb on a rack in the oven and roast for 20 minutes or until a clove feels soft when you prod it with a knife. Remove the garlic from the oven.
3 Allow to cool a little, then peel off the papery outer skin and cut the top off each clove. Squeeze the soft garlic into a small bowl and mash. Cover and store. Spread thinly.

- Cutting down on fat is the easiest way to cut down on calories. About quarter of the fat we eat comes from butter or margarine (both have the same calories). Keep them at room temperature and spread them thinly. Or swap them for low fat spreads. These generally taste much worse so you won't want to eat much of them anyway.

Garlic and Chilli Paste Ⓥ

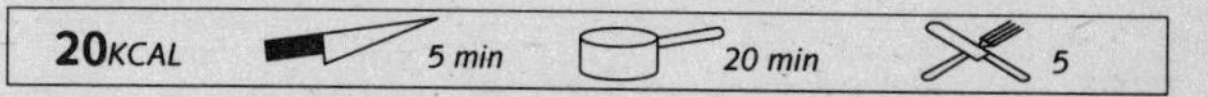

This is much like the *Roast Garlic Paste* recipe on the opposite page except you roast 2 large red chillies with the garlic bulbs. This paste is wonderful in cheese sandwiches but great too in mashed potatoes, on pasta, or in a stir-fry.

1 bulb of garlic (about 20 cloves)
2 large red chillies

1 Pre-heat oven to 200°C, 400°F, Gas 6.
2 Put the garlic bulb and chilli on a rack in the oven and roast for 20 minutes or until a clove feels soft when you prod it with a knife. Remove the garlic from the oven.
3 Allow to cool a little, then peel off the papery outer skin and cut the top off each clove. Squeeze the soft garlic into a small bowl and mash.
4 Split the roasted chillies, remove the skin and seeds and mash with the garlic or whizz in a clean coffee grinder. Cover and store. Spread thinly.

SOUPS

Calories	*Recipes*	*Page*
65	Roasted Red Pepper, Tomato and Tangerine Soup	122
65	French Onion Soup	124
90	Spinach and Nutmeg Soup	132
95	Leek and Courgette Soup	126
100	Carrot Soup with Coriander and Apricots	127
100	Italian Vegetable Soup	130
115	Curried Split Pea Soup	128
130	Toasted French Bread and Cheese	125
165	Spicy Pumpkin Soup	129
230	Minestrone Soup	131

Try to have a bowlful everyday.

A bowl of home-made soup is always delicious and full of fresh flavours. Try to a have a bowlful every day, with salad or an open sandwich as a light lunch or before your main meal as a satisfying first course. All the recipes in this chapter are served hot and are easy to make. Soup fills you up without adding too many calories and is a great way of eating more vegetables.

I've used stock cubes because I think they are the most practical way of adding flavour quickly, but I always use them at half strength – that is made up with twice as much water as it says on the pack. I find the cheapest brands the worst, so experiment with different brands until you find one with a subtle flavour. Look out, too, for the tubs of fresh stock now sold in larger supermarkets. They are much more expensive than stock cubes but the flavour is much more like home-made stock and they are worth it for some soups.

All of the soups make more than 1 portion because they all keep well, so you get at least 2 bowlfuls for your efforts and sometimes 4. It is, of course, important that you are strict with yourself and don't eat the double quantity all at once.

If you are short of time, you could make use of canned soups, too. Be sure to choose clear soups and avoid those thickened with cornflour or starch, or those with added cream. Check the can or the packet for details and read the calories carefully. Choose soups with no more than 100 calories per can or for half of a 568ml (1pt) packet. Low calorie, instant soups that you make up in a mug with boiling water are a good buy too.

Roasted Red Pepper, Tomato and Tangerine Soup Ⓥ

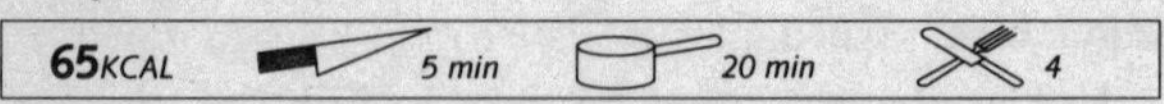

This is a sensational, fresh-tasting but simple soup. You roast the vegetables in a very hot oven, liquidise, sieve and serve. It is quite a thin soup so it's good to sip from a mug.

Allow the extra portions to cool, divide into 3 tubs, label and freeze or keep in the fridge for up to 2 days.

2 red peppers
450g (1lb) ripe tomatoes
1 tangerine or other small thin-skinned seedless orange
6 cloves of garlic
2 teaspoons olive oil
ground black pepper
850ml (1½pt) half-strength vegetable stock, made from a cube

1 Pre-heat the oven to its highest setting. Halve the red peppers and remove the core and seeds.
2 Place the red pepper, cut-side down, in a large, deep-sided roasting tin.
3 Add the tomatoes, the whole tangerine or orange and the garlic. Drizzle with oil and sprinkle with pepper.
4 Cook for 20 minutes or until the pepper and the orange are blackened and soft.
5 Remove the garlic from the tin. Snip the ends off each clove with a pair of scissors and squeeze the golden paste out, back into the mixture in the roasting tin. Take care as the paste will be hot.
6 Tip everything from the roasting tin into the liquidiser goblet. Pour half the stock into the roasting tin, stir to clean the tin and add stock to the processor. Run the machine until the mixture is blended.
7 Add the rest of the stock. Run the machine again.
8 Sieve into a small pan and discard the skin and seeds in the sieve. Bring the soup to the boil. Season and ladle a quarter of the soup into a bowl and serve hot.

French Onion Soup Ⓥ

Rich and warming, this is definitely best made with good beef stock but since nearly no one (except a chef) boils up bones for stock these days, I suggest you treat yourself to some pots of ready-made, concentrated, fresh beef stock found in supermarkets. Alternatively, and for vegetarians, look out for French onion stock cubes which intensify the soup's flavours. If you are using stock cubes, don't season until the end of cooking as stock cubes can be salty. Serve hot with some *Toasted French Bread and Cheese* (see recipe on opposite page). Remember to allow the extra portions of soup to cool, then divide into 3 tubs, label and freeze or keep in the fridge for up to 3 days.

350g (12oz) small onions
2 teaspoons olive oil
2 teaspoons fresh thyme leaves
850ml (1½pt) good, ready-made beef or vegetable stock or half-strength stock, made with a cube

1 Peel and thinly slice the onions.
2 Heat the oil in a large non-stick pan and fry the onions and the thyme over a very high heat, stirring continuously. You'll need to do this for 10 minutes to brown the onions well and give the soup it's rich golden colour.

3 Add the stock and bring to the boil. Reduce the heat, cover the pan and simmer for 10 minutes.
4 Ladle a third of the soup into a bowl and serve hot.

Toasted French Bread and Cheese Ⓥ

Traditionally, French Onion Soup is served with rounds of toasted bread and cheese. This turns a bowl of soup into a meal in itself. This cheese-topped toast can be added to a portion of the *French Onion Soup* (see recipe on opposite page) or any bowl of soup. If you are making soup for all the family, make the relevant number of toasts as quantities given here only serve one.

25g (1oz) French bread
15g (½oz) Gruyère

1 Pre-heat the grill to its highest setting.
2 Cut the French bread into two rounds and toast one side. Grate the Gruyère and divide between the untoasted sides of the bread.
3 Grill until hot and bubbling. Float in the piping hot soup. Serve straight away.

Leek and Courgette Soup Ⓥ

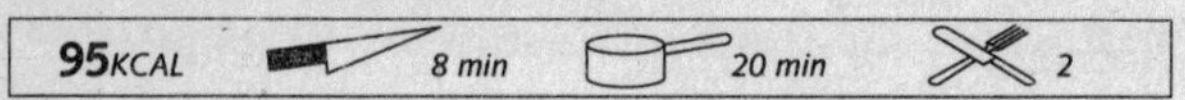

This is a satisfying soup, thickened naturally with courgettes and speckled with parsley.

Remember to allow the extra portion to cool, then spoon into a tub, label and freeze or keep in the fridge for up to 3 days.

250g (8oz) courgettes
100g (4oz) leeks
550ml (1pt) half-strength chicken or vegetable stock, made with a cube
15g (½oz) fresh parsley
150ml (¼pt) half-fat, vitamin-enriched milk

1 Peel and coarsely chop the courgettes. Slice the leeks lengthwise and rinse the leaves thoroughly to remove all the grit. Cut into rough chunks.
2 Place the courgettes and leeks in a pan with the stock. Bring to the boil, cover and simmer for 15 minutes.
3 Add the parsley and tip the soup into a liquidiser. Run the machine for 30 seconds to make a thick purée. Add the milk. Run the machine for a further 15 seconds to blend.
4 Return to the pan and bring back to the boil. Season to taste with salt and pepper. Ladle half the soup into a bowl and serve straight away.

Carrot Soup with Coriander and Apricots Ⓥ

This has a lovely light flavour and cheerful colour.

Allow the extra portion to cool, label and freeze or keep in the fridge for up to 3 days.

175g (6oz) carrots
1 small onion
½ teaspoon olive oil
1 tablespoon ground coriander
25g (1oz) ready-to-eat dried apricots
600ml (1pt) half-strength chicken or vegetable stock, made with a cube
ground black pepper
2 tablespoons chopped fresh parsley

1 Scrape the carrots and slice thinly. Peel and roughly chop the onion.
2 Heat the oil in a non-stick saucepan. Add the onion and the coriander and stir over a medium heat for 2 minutes or until the onion is softened.
3 Add the carrots, dried apricots and stock. Bring to the boil, turn down the heat, cover and simmer for 25 minutes or until the carrots are tender.
4 Tip into a liquidiser, run the machine for 30 seconds or until the soup is smooth. Add black pepper and run the machine again for 15 seconds.
5 Return the soup to the pan and bring back to the boil. Ladle half into a bowl and serve straight away.

Curried Split Pea Soup Ⓥ

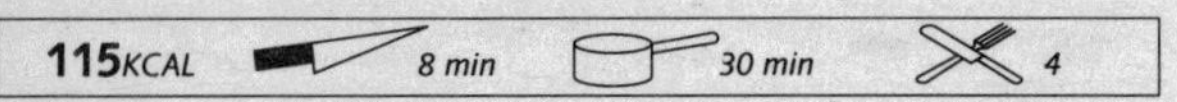

Cooked with lots of vegetables, split peas make a thick, satisfying and economical soup.

Remember to allow the extra portions to cool, then divide into 3 tubs, label and freeze or keep in the fridge for up to 3 days.

100g (4oz) yellow split peas
1 medium onion
1 carrot
½ small cauliflower
600ml (1pt) half-strength vegetable stock, made with a cube
1 teaspoon medium Madras curry powder
⅛ teaspoon ground black pepper

1 Wash the split peas in a sieve. Peel and coarsely chop the onion. Scrape and coarsely chop the carrot. Break the cauliflower up into small florets.
2 Place the vegetables into a saucepan with the vegetable stock and the curry powder. Bring to the boil, turn the heat down, cover and simmer for 30 minutes or until vegetables and lentils are soft.
3 Place in a liquidiser and run the machine until the soup is smooth. Return to the pan, add black pepper, stir well and return to the boil.
4 Ladle a quarter of the soup into a bowl and serve straight away.

Spicy Pumpkin Soup Ⓥ

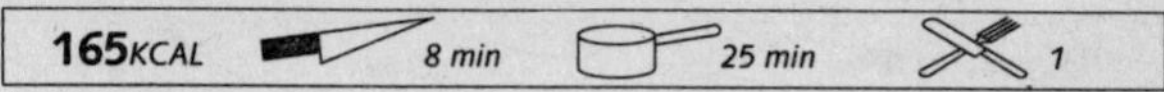

Pumpkin is a wonderful vegetable. The bright orange flesh cooks to a soft pulp looking like mashed swede, and makes a great purée with a cheery colour and mild flavour. If you've never prepared pumpkin before, you just cut it in half as you would a melon and scoop out the seeds. Cut into manageable slices and cut off the outer rind, cutting the flesh into small cubes.

1 medium onion
450g (1lb) pumpkin flesh, weighed without the skin
⅛ teaspoon ground nutmeg
⅛ teaspoon ground cloves
⅛ teaspoon coarsely ground black pepper
850ml (1½pt) good stock

1 Peel and coarsely chop the onion. Cut the pumpkin into small chunks.
2 Heat the oil in a non-stick pan and fry the onion for 5 minutes over a high heat, stirring continuously. Add the nutmeg, cloves and pepper and cook for 30 seconds.
3 Add the pumpkin and the stock. Bring to the boil, cover and simmer for 20 minutes until the pumpkin in tender when you prod it with a fork.
4 Liquidise until smooth, return to the pan and bring to the boil. Taste, season if needed, and serve.

Italian Vegetable Soup Ⓥ

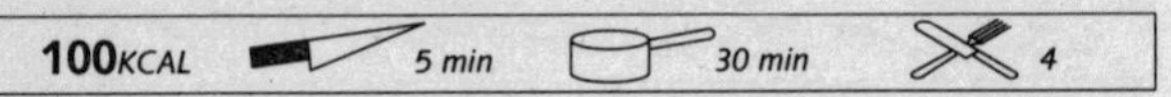

Look out for stew packs of root vegetables which usually contain 2 carrots, 1 leek, 1 onion and a small swede. They are ideal for making this soup.

This is one of those soups that freezes well. Alternatively, it is just as good kept in the fridge and heated up the following day, so allow the extra portions to cool, then divide into 3 tubs, label and freeze or keep in the fridge for up to 3 days.

2 small carrots weighing 125g (5oz)
1 small leek weighing 75g (3oz)
1 small onion weighing 75g (3oz)
½ small swede weighing 250g (8oz)
2 sticks of celery weighing 100g (4oz)
2 teaspoons olive oil
1.1litres (2pt) half-strength chicken or vegetable stock, made with a cube
415g (14oz) can tomatoes with herbs
100g (4oz) green beans, fresh or frozen
4 tablespoons chopped fresh parsley

1 Scrape the carrot and dice into small pieces. Slice the leek lengthwise and rinse well to get rid of any grit between the leaves. Slice it lengthwise again and chop. Peel and chop the onion. Thickly peel the swede and dice into small pieces. Rinse and chop the celery.

2 Heat the oil in a large non-stick saucepan and fry the onion and leek over a medium heat for 2 to 3 minutes to soften them. Add the carrot, swede, celery, stock and canned tomatoes.
3 Bring to the boil, turn down the heat, cover and simmer for 25 minutes.
4 Cut the beans into short lengths and add to the soup. Simmer for 5 minutes. Add the parsley.
5 Ladle a quarter of the soup into a bowl and serve.

Minestrone Soup Ⓥ

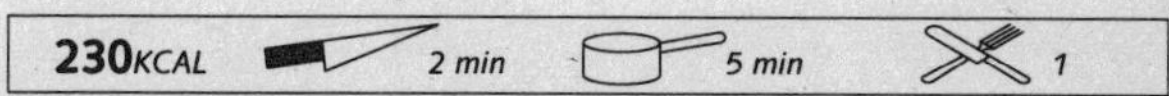

It's amazing how non-vegetable eaters love *Minestrone Soup*. By adding some pasta, beans and freshly grated cheese to fresh vegetable soup it becomes a filling main meal.

1 portion Italian Vegetable Soup (see opposite page)
25g (1oz) cooked pasta
25g (1oz) canned cannellini beans
15g (½oz) grated fresh Parmesan cheese

1 Place the *Italian Vegetable Soup* in a small pan and bring to the boil.
2 Add the pasta and beans and simmer for 1 minute to heat through.
3 Ladle into a soup bowl and scatter with Parmesan. Serve straight away.

Spinach and Nutmeg Soup Ⓥ

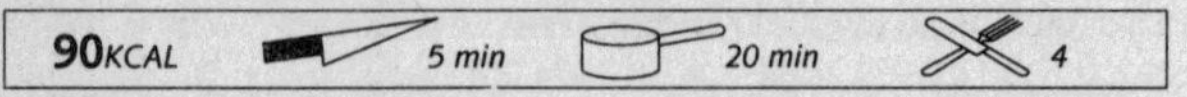

Young fresh spinach leaves – often pre-packed in handy bags – are good to use when in season, but I find frozen spinach works well, too, for soups. Spinach soup is full of iron, so it's a good vegetable to choose if you don't eat much red meat. This recipe makes a thin soup with a vivid colour.

Remember to allow the extra portions to cool, then divide into 3 tubs, label and freeze or keep in the fridge for up to 3 days.

1 onion
2 cloves of garlic
250g (8oz) small courgettes
1 teaspoon olive oil
350g (12oz) fresh young spinach or 450g (1lb) frozen spinach leaf
850ml (1½pt) half-strength chicken or vegetable stock, made with a cube
300ml (1½pt) skimmed milk
1 teaspoon fresh lemon juice
¼ teaspoon fresh grated nutmeg

1 Peel and finely chop the onion and the garlic. Peel and slice the courgettes.
2 Heat the oil in a non-stick saucepan. Add the onion and garlic and fry over a medium heat for 2 minutes until softened but not browned. Add the

courgettes and the spinach and cook for a further 1 minute until the fresh spinach wilts.

3 Add the stock. Bring to the boil, reduce the heat, cover and simmer for 15 minutes.

4 Add the milk, lemon juice and nutmeg and pour into a liquidiser. Run the machine for 30 seconds or until the mixture is smooth.

5 Return to the pan, bring back to the boil, taste and add seasoning if necessary, and serve. Ladle a quarter of the soup into a bowl and serve straight away.

• If you are trying to lose weight, don't weigh yourself every day. Once a week, at the same time, wearing the same clothes is plenty. If you are a woman, weighing once a month will give you a clearer picture as your weight can rise by several pounds before your period. Lots of women seem to crave chocolate- and sugar-rich foods at this time too, so be prepared. You'll find that weighing yourself in the morning, with no clothes on, after a period gives the best result.

SALADS

Eat real meal-in-a-bowl sorts of salads.

Of all the foods that we should eat, it is probably salad which fills most of us with dread. Be positive! Forget limp lettuce and tomato quarters on the side of the plate. I am talking about real 'meal-in-a-bowl' sort of salads which are big on flavour. Think of handsome mixtures of lovely fresh ingredients like Stilton with plums and walnuts, mangetout with oranges and sesame oil or tart Roquefort cheese with tiny fresh spinach leaves and black grapes. Most of the salads in this chapter are the star turn of the meal, not an also-ran added as an afterthought.

Buy fresh ingredients in small quantities and use them up quickly. Look out for tomatoes grown in the sun or varieties specially grown for flavour and try to find green beans, sugar snaps and mange-tout, tight heads of crisp white cauliflower and tiny button mushrooms to add variety to your salads. Bags of mixed lettuce leaves are so good for feeding just one person, and adding some prawns, roasted chicken, poached salmon, diced smoked ham, flaked tuna fish or hard-boiled eggs puts you well on your way to a memorable meal that's a million miles from the dull salad you dread.

Melon, Cucumber, Tomato and Mint Salad Ⓥ

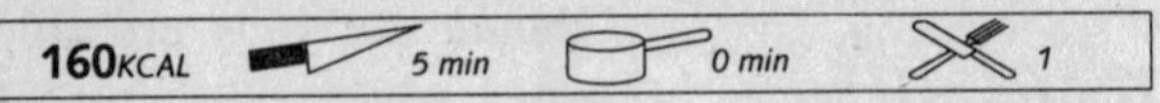

I first had this as a starter at a friend's house one summer evening and it's one of those improbable combinations that really works. It makes a very refreshing, fresh-tasting salad which is as good as the ingredients that you put in it – so choose a ripe, well-flavoured melon and tomatoes. Serve as a starter, instead of soups, or as a salad with cold roast chicken or cooked peeled prawns. Some crusty white bread is good with it too, to mop up the juices. Chill for 30 minutes before serving.

½ small, ripe honeydew melon
3 ripe plum tomatoes
7.5cm (3in) piece of cucumber
1 spring onion
8 small fresh mint leaves
salt
ground black pepper
1 teaspoon olive oil
1 teaspoon red wine vinegar

1 Cut the melon half in three and scrape out the seeds with a teaspoon. Cut the melon flesh off the skin and cut into small cubes.
2 Cut the tomatoes into small chunks. Dice the cucumber into large pieces. Strip the outside leaf from the spring onion and trim off the roots; cut

the green and white parts into short lengths. Finely shred the mint.

3 Mix the melon, tomatoes, cucumber, spring onion and mint in a large glass serving bowl. Season with salt and a little black pepper. Add the oil and vinegar, toss lightly, cover and chill for 30 minutes to allow the flavours to mingle. Serve cold.

Carrot Salad with Lemon and Honey Ⓥ

This is a good salad to serve when you need a change from lettuce. It's crisp and fresh (so long as you don't use tired old carrots) and is a great salad-on-the-side to go with cold meats, strong cheeses, barbecued or grilled foods and baked potatoes.

250g (8oz) fresh young carrots
1 tablespoon chopped fresh parsley
1 tablespoon fresh lemon juice
1 tablespoon unsweetened orange juice
1 teaspoon clear honey
1 teaspoon olive oil

1 Coarsely grate the carrots.

2 Spoon the parsley, lemon juice, orange juice, honey and oil into a small bowl and whisk together with a fork.

3 Add the carrots and stir well to coat.

Nearly Niçoise

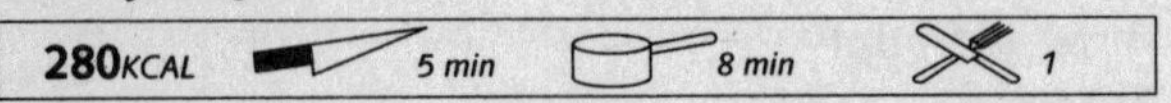

There are lots of different versions of this but essentially so long as you have green beans, hard-boiled egg and tuna in it you've got the basis of a jolly tasty salad from the south of France. Buy the beans ready trimmed to save you time. If you have some small cold, boiled new potatoes you could halve them and mix them in; 75g (3oz) of these would add an extra 75 calories. If you have opened a can of anchovies, use the rest to make the *Black Olive Paste* on page 161.

1 egg, size 3
175g (6oz) trimmed green beans
50g (2oz) canned tuna
2 canned anchovy fillets
6 leaves of little gem lettuce
5 black olives
1 teaspoon extra virgin olive oil

1 Place the egg in a small pan, cover with cold water and bring the water to the boil. Set the timer for 5 minutes, reduce the heat to a simmer and allow the eggs to simmer constantly until the pinger goes. Lift the egg out with a slotted spoon and cover with cold running water.
2 Add the green beans to the simmering water. Return to the boil and simmer for 2 minutes so that

beans are hot but still crisp. Drain.

3 Tap the rounded end of the egg on the work surface to crack the shell. Peel off the shell, rinse the egg again and cut into quarters.

4 Drain the tuna and the anchovy fillets and rinse under cold water. Leave the tuna as chunks and cut the anchovy fillets in half lengthwise.

5 Line a plate with the lettuce, top with the beans, tuna, olives and finally the egg. Arrange a piece of anchovy fillet over each egg and drizzle the whole salad with the olive oil. Serve at room temperature.

Four lousy excuses for not taking exercise

- I'm too busy – make time. If getting fitter or losing weight is really important to you then make exercise a pleasure not a chore.
- I'm too old – it's never too late. Anyone can get fitter or lose weight. You are never too old to get out of puff a little. You don't have take up squash or jogging just walk a little faster or a little further.
- I'm too fat – all the more reason to spend less time eating (and taking in calories) and more time exercising (and using up calories). And there's evidence that you may still be burning up more calories than you usually would, as much as 24 hours after you've finished exercising.
- I'm too tired – using energy gives you energy. It's inactivity that's draining. Get up and go, go, go.

Sort-of-Caesar Salad Ⓥ

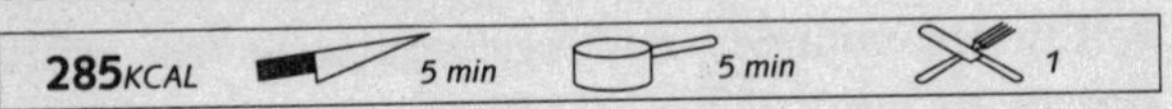

This is another of those classics that has lots of variations. I first enjoyed it in Los Angeles where a portion used to come in a bowl with enough to serve 4 people! You must use Cos lettuce and it should have crisp cheesy croutons. Some versions have anchovies in. Mine doesn't but add a couple of canned anchovies, drained and rinsed, if you like.

½ small Cos lettuce
15g (½oz) Parmesan cheese
1 thin slice white bread weighing 25g (1oz)
25g (1oz) Boursin cheese with garlic and herbs
4 tablespoons skimmed milk

1 Pre-heat the grill to its highest setting. Separate the lettuce leaves, rinse under cold water, shake and tear into small pieces. Toss into a serving bowl.
2 Finely grate the Parmesan. Toast the bread under the grill on one side only. Place it toasted side down on the work surface and cover the untoasted side with the Parmesan. Grill for 1 or 2 minutes until the edges are brown and the cheese has melted. Cut into very small squares about 1cm (¼in) across. Scatter over the lettuce.
3 To make the dressing: place the Boursin on a plate and mash with a fork. Add the milk a spoonful at a time and mash to a smooth sauce.

Place in the microwave oven and warm through on full power (100%) for 20 seconds until mixture is runny. (Alternatively, heat gently in a small non-stick saucepan.)

4 Pour over the salad. Serve straight away.

Grilled Goats' Cheese and Pine Nuts Ⓥ

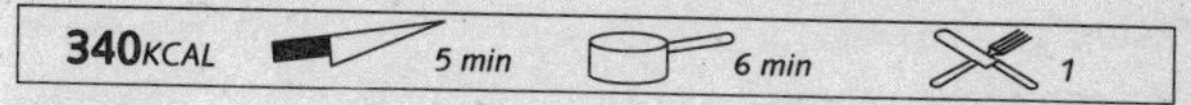

This is so simple and so delicious. It's a very satisfying and stylish French salad – you won't feel cheated after this for lunch.

10g (⅓oz) pine kernels
40g (1½oz) thin baguette or French stick
25g (1oz) goats' cheese
½ bag washed Lamb's lettuce
1 teaspoon hazelnut oil

1 Pre-heat the grill to its highest setting. Put the pine kernels on a sheet of foil under the grill and watch carefully, shaking the foil, to toast the nuts until golden.

2 Cut the bread into 5 small slices. Spread with cheese and pop under the grill. Toast until golden.

3 Meanwhile wash the lettuce and shake dry. Arrange in a large soup plate or serving bowl. Add the cheesey toasts and the toasted pine kernels and drizzle with the hazelnut oil. Serve.

White Stilton, Plum and Walnut Salad Ⓥ

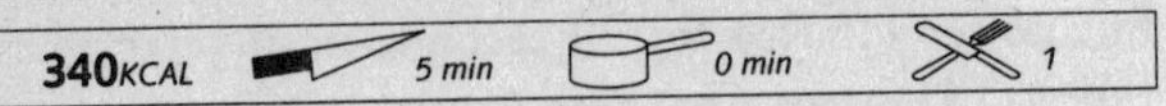

Choose an old-fashioned country plum in season for the very best flavour and some fresh, crumbly white Stilton for a change. This is also lovely with some of the other crumbly-textured, English cheeses like Cheshire, Lancashire and Wensleydale.

3 ripe eating plums
40g (1½oz) white Stilton
½ small Cos lettuce
2 tablespoons apple juice
1 teaspoon olive oil
¼ teaspoon ready-made English mustard
Worcestershire sauce
10g (⅓oz) walnut pieces

1 Halve and stone the plums and cut into small chunks. Cut the Stilton into small cubes.
2 Wash the lettuce leaves, shake dry and tear into small pieces. Toss them in a serving bowl.
3 To make the dressing: spoon the apple juice, olive oil and mustard into a cup. Add a dash of Worcestershire sauce and whisk well with a fork. Pour over the lettuce and toss well to coat the leaves.
4 Scatter the plums, Stilton and walnuts over the lettuce. Serve straight away.

Feta with Black Olives and Cos Ⓥ

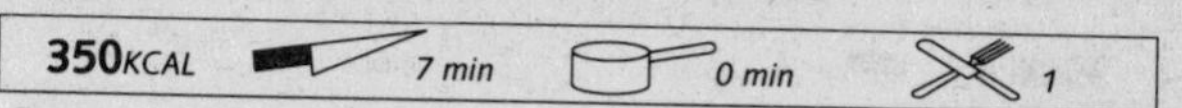

I find that Cos is one of the few lettuces with any real flavour as well as a satisfying crunchy texture. Choose the freshest, crispest lettuce you can find and throw away any soft leaves on the outside (or make them into soup). Tear the lettuce into small pieces and eat the salad as soon as possible.

½ Cos lettuce
75g (3oz) feta cheese
25g (1oz) Greek kalamati olives, stoned
1 beefsteak tomato
7.5cm (3in) piece of cucumber
1 teaspoon extra virgin olive oil

1 Separate the leaves from the lettuce and rinse them well under cold running water; shake dry, tear into pieces and toss in a mixing bowl.
2 Drain the feta from its liquid and dice into very small pieces about 1cm (¼in) across. Halve the olives. Cut the tomato in quarters and then into small chunks. Stand the cucumber on its cut end and cut lengthwise into 8 sticks, then into short lengths.
3 Add the feta, olives, tomatoes and cucumber to the lettuce. Drizzle with the oil and toss lightly to mix. Serve straight away.

Mangetout, Orange and Sesame Salad

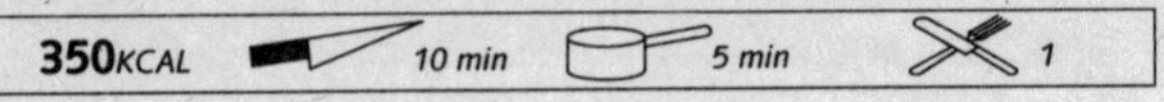

Frozen mangetout are a good freezer standby as the quality is very good and the price reasonable all year round. I wish you could buy ready-roasted duck portions because this salad would also be delicious with duck. Still it is good with chicken and you get more to eat for your calories that way.

175g (6oz) mangetout, fresh or frozen
1 orange
1 thin stick green celery
75g (3oz) roasted, boneless, skinless chicken breast
50g (2oz) fresh beansprouts
½ Cos lettuce
1 teaspoon sesame oil (or toasted sesame oil)

1 If using fresh mangetout, snip their ends off.
2 Bring a pan of water to the boil and plunge mangetout in. Simmer for 2 minutes and drain.
3 Coarsely grate rind from orange. Stand orange on a plate and cut off white pith using a sharp knife. Cut into segments, catching any juices on the plate.
4 Finely slice the celery. Cut the chicken into cubes. Rinse beansprouts and lettuce. Shake dry.
5 Put 1 teaspoon orange rind in a serving bowl with any juices and the sesame oil. Add the mangetout, orange segments, celery, beansprouts, lettuce and chicken and toss well to mix.

Walnut, Roquefort and Black Grape Salad Ⓥ

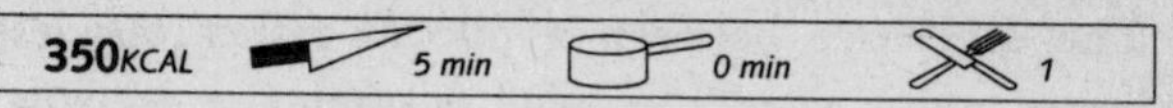

This is such a good salad. It's full of very grown-up ingredients that taste great together. The spinach must be fresh, not frozen, and it must be the tender little leaves, nothing coarse and stringy please. If the last time you used walnuts was to make a cake, then treat yourself to a new packet. Walnuts lose their flavour and go bitter if you keep them too long. Look out for Californian walnuts which are sweeter-tasting. Buy small bags as you need them.

75g (3oz) fresh baby spinach leaves
15g (½oz) walnut halves
50g (2oz) small, seedless black or red grapes
50g (2oz) Roquefort cheese

1 Half fill a basin with cold water. Add the spinach leaves and swish about gently to rinse. Shake dry, a handful at a time, and toss in a large serving bowl. Tear up any that are very large.
2 Halve the walnuts and the grapes. Cut the Roquefort into tiny cubes.
3 Add the walnuts and the grapes to the spinach and scatter the Roquefort on top. Serve straight away.

Salad Dressings

The difference between a pile of rather tasteless leaves and a wonderful salad is often the dressing. And if you're the sort who can eat a big bowl of rabbit food with just a squeeze of lemon then you're probably thin already. For the rest of us, it's the olive oil or the blue cheese dressing that makes the greens palatable. Here are 4 handy recipes for when the greens need a lift.

Thousand Island Dressing Ⓥ

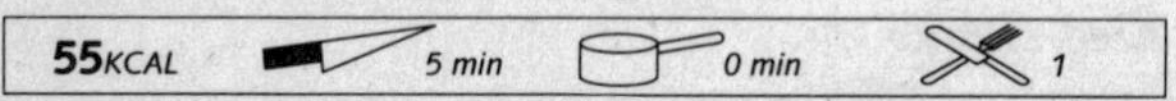

A classic flavour and one that I use if I'm making a 'chef's salad' with cold roast chicken, tuna or hard-boiled eggs and lots of crunchy Iceberg lettuce, young spinach and watercress. Great as a dip with raw cauliflower florets.

4 teaspoons reduced fat mayonnaise
2 teaspoons tomato ketchup
dash Worcestershire sauce
squeeze fresh lemon juice
2 teaspoons water
ground black pepper

1 Mix the mayonnaise, ketchup, Worcestershire sauce, lemon juice and water together. Season with pepper and spoon over the salad just before serving.

Herb and Garlic Dressing Ⓥ

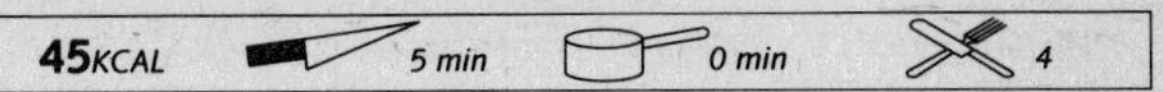

Spoon into baked potatoes, over roast vegetables or crisp salads, and use as a dip for sticks of carrot and celery, raw cauliflower florets and other vegetables. Also good spooned over pasta for a speedy sauce.

1 clove of garlic
100g (4oz) silken tofu
4 tablespoons Greek yoghurt
1 tablespoon chopped fresh chives
2 tablespoons chopped fresh parsley
1 tablespoon half-fat, vitamin-enriched milk

1 Peel and halve the garlic.
2 Place the garlic, tofu, yoghurt, chives, parsley and milk in a liquidiser goblet. Add 4 tablespoons of water and run the machine until the mixture is blended.
3 Scrape down any mixture which escaped the blades and run the machine again. Use a spatula to get all the mixture out into a serving dish, cover and store in the fridge for up to 3 days.

- Fresh herbs are calorie free and can add a wonderful variety of flavours to all sorts of food. Most will thrive in pots all year round and it's easy and cheap to grow your own.

Blue Cheese Dressing Ⓥ

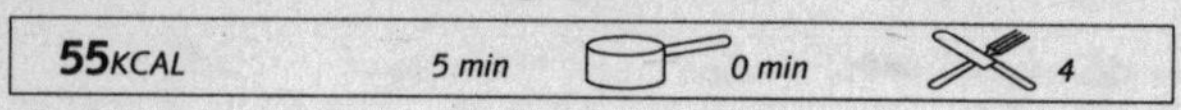

I must confess that I normally list tofu, along with sheeps' eyes and steamed jellyfish, as food that I would rather not eat twice. However, silken tofu, the smooth Japanese sort, has its merits being low in fat, high in protein, as smooth as yoghurt and bland to taste. Add some pungent blue cheese, a shake of good vinegar and some seasoning and you have a generous portion of blue cheese dressing for a meagre number of calories. Spoon into baked potatoes, over roast vegetables (especially beetroot roasted in their skins), over salads and use as a dip for crisp sticks of raw vegetables.

100g (4oz) silken tofu
40g (1½oz) Danish blue cheese
1 teaspoon white wine vinegar
pinch dry mustard powder
4 tablespoons half-fat, vitamin-enriched milk

1 Place the tofu, blue cheese, vinegar and mustard powder in a liquidiser goblet. Add 4 tablespoons of water and the milk and run the machine until the mixture is blended. (The mixture is very thick.)
2 Scrape down any mixture which escaped the blades and run the machine again. Use a spatula to get all the mixture out into a serving dish, cover and store in the fridge for up to 3 days.

French Dressing Ⓥ

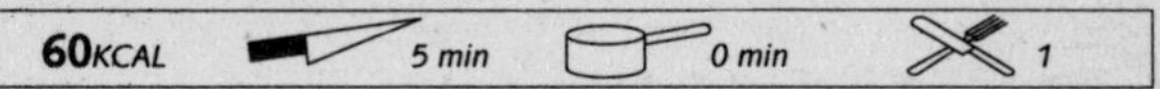

If you can't face salad or vegetables without a decent dressing, then don't! Make a good dressing with lovely oil, good vinegar and enjoy it. It's lovely over leafy lettuce, slices of tomato and cucumber, lightly cooked green beans or broccoli, cauliflower and new potatoes, boiled pasta and rice, grilled fish and chicken. Make this just before you need it.

1 teaspoon olive oil
1 teaspoon red or white wine vinegar
salt
ground black pepper
¼ teaspoon Dijon mustard

1 Spoon the oil and vinegar into a small cup. Add salt and pepper, the mustard and 1 teaspoon of cold water. Whisk lightly with a fork and pour over salad just before serving.

- 1 tablespoon of oil has 120 calories so get a teaspoon out and measure oil carefully. Although olive oil has been hailed as a good-for-you oil and part of the Mediterranean diet, don't be tempted to pour it from the bottle onto your food. It may be a 'healthier' oil but the calories are the same as for other oils.

THINGS ON TOAST

Calories	*Recipes*	*Page*
80	Smoked Salmon Pâté	154
100	Chicken Liver Pâté	152
115	Smoked Mackerel Pâté	155
145	Garlicky Roasted Mushrooms	156
185	Black Olive Paste	161
205	Sardines, Tomatoes and Parmesan	160
255	Smoked Ham and Pineapple	158
265	Pesto, Edam and Tomato	158
300	Baked Beans, Dijon and Gruyère	157
335	Stilton, Celery and Apple	159

Ingredients for toasts can come straight from the cupboard.

A little something on toast is quick to put together and makes a really tasty calorie-counted lunch or snack – from simple, but substantial, beans on toast (I add Dijon mustard and Gruyère to mine) to quick mix pâtés that keep well in the fridge for impromptu snacks, sandwiches and suppers. Always choose good bread as a base for your toasts, and serve them with a bowl of fresh vegetable soup or with a generous salad of crisp, raw vegetables.

Ingredients for toasts can come straight from the storecupboard, so use sardines canned in oil, baked beans or well-flavoured sauces, or from the fridge, with cheeses, smoked fish or ham making good toppings. Cheese on toast is an old favourite but ring the changes from Cheddar and add some low calorie ingredients to make it go further. Try Stilton with celery and apple (wonderful on walnut bread), or toast spread with pesto and topped with ripe tomatoes and Edam with black peppercorns. Delicious!

Shop-bought pâtés are often high in fat, but the three home-made recipes in this chapter give a good-sized portion for a sensible number of calories. The *Smoked Mackerel Pâté* (see recipe on page 155) is also good as a filling in a baked potato. The pâté recipes make more than one portion but they keep well and what you don't eat on toast one day you could have in a sandwich or with a salad another. They are also a handy starter if you have friends coming for supper.

Chicken Liver Pâté

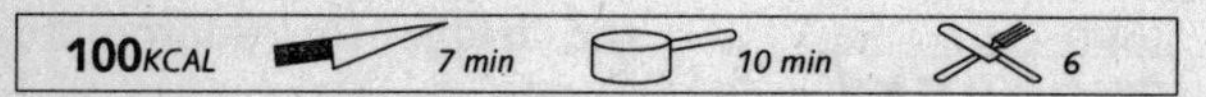

Chicken livers are great value and full of iron. They are quick to cook and make a delicious paste to spread on warm toast or crackers. Use a whole tub of chicken livers at a time as this pâté keeps in the fridge for up to 3 days or freezes for up to 1 month. Allow to defrost thoroughly before eating. Serve each pot with 1 slice of unbuttered toast, some Lambs' lettuce or a French-style salad from one of those bags of ready-mixed salad leaves.

250g (8oz) tub frozen chicken livers, defrosted
50g (2oz) smoked, streaky bacon
1 small onion
1 plump clove of garlic
1 teaspoon olive oil
15g (½oz) unsalted Dutch butter
1 teaspoon fresh thyme leaves
salt
ground black pepper

1 Tip the livers into a sieve and rinse. Remove any stringy white bits. Remove rind, if any, from the bacon and chop roughly. Skin and roughly chop the onion and garlic.
2 Heat the oil and butter in a non-stick pan. Add the onion and the garlic and fry for 3 minutes to soften. Add the bacon and cook for further 2 minutes. Add the chicken livers, thyme and 5 tablespoons of water and cook for a further 5 minutes until livers are cooked through.
3 Cool slightly, then tip the mixture and all the pan juices into a food processor. Season with salt and pepper and run the machine to make a smooth paste.
4 Spoon into 6 individual pots and smooth the top of the pâté. Cover and chill.

• Eat food slowly. Think about it, savour the flavours and chew it well. Try to eat regularly – a little and often is good practice. Don't skip meals and think you will save yourself some calories – you'll end up feeling hungry a couple of hours after meal time and then you're vulnerable to a snack attack.

Smoked Salmon Pâté

Look out for bags of off-cuts and salmon trimmings. If you are lucky enough to have a fishmonger near you, ask him – otherwise try a delicatessen. Off-cuts are not better than slices of salmon for this, just cheaper. This pâté keeps in the fridge for up to 3 days or freezes for up to 1 month. Allow to defrost thoroughly before serving.

½ small lemon
100g (4oz) smoked salmon
50g (2oz) smooth, reduced fat soft cheese
⅛ teaspoon fresh ground nutmeg
ground black pepper

1 Grate rind from lemon and squeeze out juice. Roughly chop the salmon.
2 Place the smoked salmon, 1 teaspoon of the lemon rind and 2 teaspoons of the juice in a food processor with the cheese. Add the nutmeg and some ground black pepper.
3 Run the machine until the mixture is smooth. Divide into 3 little pots. Cover and chill.

Smoked Mackerel Pâté

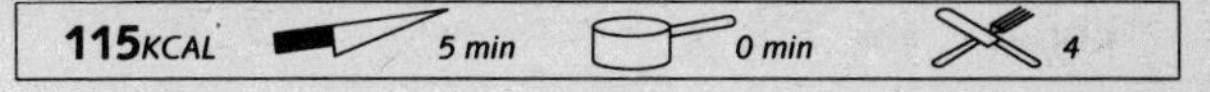

Smoked mackerel has a rich, strong flavour that needs the yoghurt and the horseradish sauce to lighten it. This pâté will freeze well or will keep, covered, in the fridge for up to 5 days. Serve with a generous salad of lettuce and slices of crisp red eating apple. It's good, too, on hot, unbuttered toast or spread onto celery sticks.

175g (6oz) smoked mackerel with peppercorns
2 tablespoons Greek yoghurt
1 teaspoon creamed horseradish sauce
ground black pepper to taste

1 Flake the mackerel off the skin with a knife and tip the flakes of fish into the food processor.
2 Add the yoghurt, horseradish and pepper and run the machine until the mixture is smooth.
3 Divide into 4 individual pots. Cover and chill.

• The decision to lose weight is in your hands. Take control. Ask yourself 'Do I want to be thinner more than I want that family-size bag of sour cream and chive crisps?'. The answer is 'YES'.

Garlicky Roasted Mushrooms Ⓥ

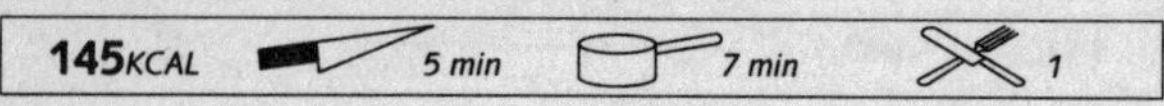

Mushrooms roasted over a fierce heat so that they are seared and golden give a wonderful savoury smell and bags of flavour for relatively few calories. Try adding some finely diced red pepper with the mushrooms at the start of the cooking.

100g (4oz) brown cap or chestnut mushrooms
1 clove of garlic
1 teaspoon olive oil
2 teaspoons fresh mixed herbs such as thyme, parsley and oregano
150ml (¼pt) half-strength French onion or vegetable stock made with a cube
1 small slice wholemeal bread weighing 25g (1oz)

1 Wipe and quarter the mushrooms. Peel and crush the garlic.
2 Heat the oil in a non-stick saucepan and fry the onions, garlic and herbs over a high heat, stirring continuously with a wooden spoon, for 5 minutes or until the mushrooms are golden. Reduce heat, add the stock, cover the pan and allow to stew in their own juices for a further 2 minutes. Lift the lid off and allow the stock to reduce by half at the end of cooking.
3 Meanwhile, toast the bread. Serve the mushrooms on toast with their juices poured over.

Baked Beans, Dijon and Gruyère Ⓥ

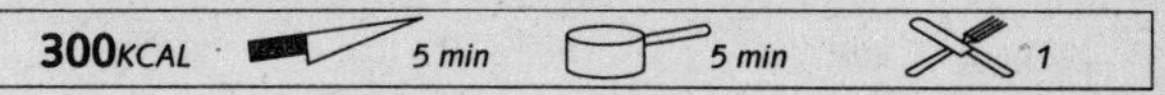

You really can't beat beans on toast for quick, filling, good-for-you snack. Add a bit of flavouring and some melted cheese and you have a very satisfying supper. Vegetarians should use an anchovy-free Worcestershire sauce or leave it out altogether.

175g (6oz) sugar- and salt-reduced baked beans in tomato sauce
1 teaspoon Dijon mustard
Worcestershire sauce
15g (½oz) Gruyère
1 thick slice wholemeal bread weighing 50g (2oz)

1 Pre-heat the grill to its highest setting.
2 Tip the baked beans into a small saucepan and add the mustard and a dash of Worcestershire sauce. Heat gently, stirring. Bring to the boil and simmer for 1 minute to heat through.
3 Grate the Gruyère coarsely.
4 Toast one side of the bread and turn it over. Arrange on a heatproof serving plate and top with the hot bean mixture.
5 Scatter the grated cheese on top and pop under the grill for a further minute until the cheese is bubbling and melted. Serve straight away.

Pesto, Edam and Tomato Ⓥ

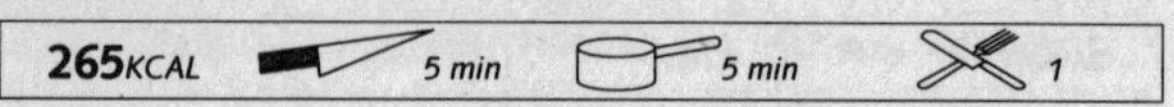

Edam is a really good cooking cheese. What it lacks in flavour it makes up for in texture, once it's melted. This toast is good cut into cubes and tossed in a salad or served with a bowl of soup.

50g (2oz) Ciabatta (Italian olive oil bread)
1 large ripe tomato
25g (1oz) Edam cheese
1 teaspoon pesto sauce

1 Pre-heat the grill to its highest setting.
2 Slice the Ciabatta in half and open out. Thinly slice the tomato and the cheese.
3 Thinly spread the pesto over the cut side of the bread. Cover with the tomatoes and the cheese.
4 Grill for 1 minute or until the cheese is hot and bubbly. Serve straight away.

Smoked Ham and Pineapple

This is good with canned pineapple and great with fresh. Serve with a green leafy salad and some sliced tomatoes with lots of ground black pepper on them. Do trim all the visible white fat from the outside of the ham.

25g (1oz) Austrian smoked cheese
1 slice crusty white bread weighing 25g (1oz)
1 slice lean, smoked ham weighing 25g (1oz)
1 canned pineapple ring, drained

1 Pre-heat the grill to its highest setting. Thinly slice the cheese.
2 Toast one side of the bread. Top with the ham, the pineapple ring and the cheese and grill until the cheese is hot and bubbly. Serve straight away.

Stilton, Celery and Apple Ⓥ

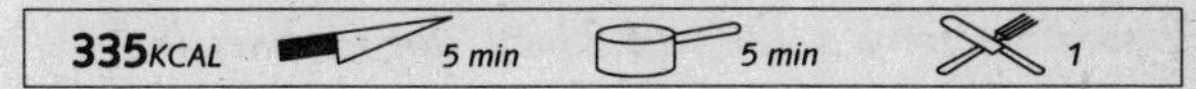

This is fabulous on walnut bread but works just as well on something brown and substantial.

1 sweet red-skinned eating apple
1 stick celery
(45g) 1½oz mature Stilton cheese
1 slice rye or oatmeal bread weighing 25g (1oz)

1 Pre-heat the grill to its highest setting.
2 Core and slice the apple. Wash and finely slice the celery. Crumble the Stilton.
3 Toast one side of the bread and turn over.
4 Cover with the apple slices, top with the celery and scatter the Stilton over. Return to the grill for 1 minute or until the Stilton melts. Serve hot.

Sardines, Tomatoes and Parmesan

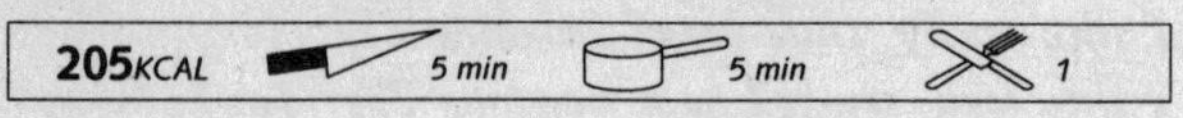

Sardines are a useful source of calcium which we all need for healthy bones and teeth. If you don't drink much milk, then you should make sure you eat lots of sardines instead. They are cheap so keep a can handy in the cupboard. (You should find that you have two sardines left in the can after making this recipe. Tip them into a bowl, cover and keep them in the fridge. Mash them for a sandwich the next day or use to fill a baked potato.)

2 sardines from a 120g (4.23oz) can sardines in sunflower oil
squeeze of fresh lemon juice
1 small slice wholemeal bread weighing 25g (1oz)
1 medium tomato
ground black pepper
15g (½oz) fresh Parmesan cheese

1 Pre-heat the grill to its highest setting. Rinse the sardines under cold running water. Drain and mash with a few drops of fresh lemon juice.
2 Toast the bread on one side and spread the sardines on the untoasted side. Slice the tomato into 4 and arrange slices over sardines. Add pepper.
3 Grate Parmesan and arrange over the tomatoes.
4 Return to the grill and heat until the cheese is bubbling and melted. Serve straight away.

Black Olive Paste

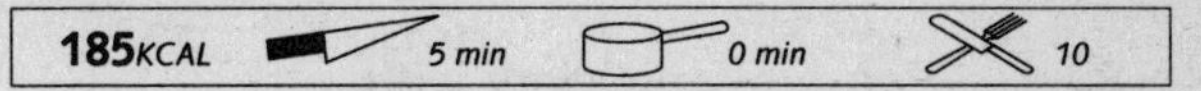

This paste makes a pungent, strongly flavoured topping which, spread thinly on good crusty bread, is a cheaper calorie option than butter or margarine. I use this in sandwiches and salad dressings; on grilled chicken and fish and to make steamed vegetables more exciting. Mix it in the food processor and store in the fridge for up to 2 weeks.

200g (7oz) can pitted black olives in brine
2x50g (2oz) cans anchovy fillets in oil
50g (2oz) drained capers
1 clove of garlic
½ teaspoon Dijon mustard
1 tablespoon extra virgin olive oil
1 teaspoon fresh lemon juice
2 tablespoons chopped fresh parsley
freshly ground black pepper

1 Drain the olives, you should have about 100g (4oz). Drain the anchovy fillets and rinse in water.
2 Put the olives, anchovy fillets, capers and garlic into the food processor. Run the machine until the olives are coarsely chopped.
3 Add the mustard, olive oil, lemon juice, parsley and a good grinding of black pepper and run the machine again to make a finely chopped paste.
4 Transfer to a clean, screw-topped jar and chill.

VEGETABLES

Try to be adventurous and try new vegetables.

Of all the foods that you choose to eat in a day, I think it is the vegetables which are vital. If you are overweight, my guess is that you are not eating enough fresh, raw or lightly cooked veggies. Vegetables can make the difference between feeling hungry and feeling satisfied. They are the key to healthy eating and this will help you achieve and keep the weight you want to be.

I think everyone could do with a rethink about their attitude to vegetables. Don't think of them as an afterthought, choose them first. *Plan the vegetables and then choose what else you will have to accompany them.* Be adventurous and try vegetables that you have previously not chosen or thought you didn't like. Perhaps your dislike stems from the fact that they weren't cooked properly or weren't well flavoured. Nothing in this chapter is dull and you can forget plain boiled carrots and steamed cabbage. Try instead the *Broccoli Stalks with Blue Cheese* (see recipe on page 175) or the *Cauliflower with Sweet and Sour Sauce* (see recipe on page 176) and you'll see what I mean. Most of these recipes cook in under 10 minutes and they give you lots of goodness and not many calories.

Everyone should aim to eat at least 3 or 4 portions of vegetables a day – that is, 100g (4oz) portions – and you should aim to mix up the green, leafy ones like spinach and cabbage with root ones like carrots, potatoes and swede in order to get a mix of vitamins. Be aware of the starchy ones like sweetcorn, beetroot and potatoes which are higher in calories. Cook vegetables lightly and serve them without any extra butter or margarine. A combination of cooked vegetables as your main meal, a bowl of fresh vegetable soup and a crisp and colourful salad, every day, will have to become a way of life if you are to lose weight permanently. Work on it. Start here.

Leek Purée with Allspice Ⓥ

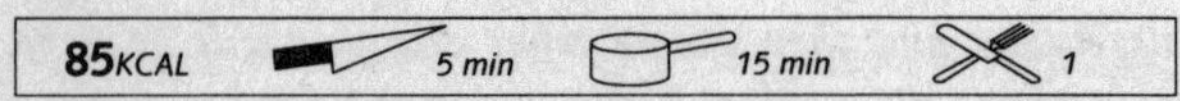

This makes a lovely soft green mash and is lovely accompanied by a bacon chop, grilled chicken or fish, or slices of roast meat. It freezes well so I usually make plenty and freeze what I don't need.

250g (8oz) young leeks
⅛ teaspoon ground allspice
⅛ teaspoon black pepper
2 tablespoons Greek yoghurt

1 Trim the root from the leeks. Slit them lengthwise and rinse under cold water to wash out any grit between the leaves. Cut them into chunks.

2 Steam the leeks in a colander over a pan of simmering water for 15 minutes, or until the leek feels soft when prodded with a knife.
3 Tip the leek into a food processor and run the machine until the mixture is a smooth green purée.
4 Add the allspice, pepper and yoghurt and run the machine again to mix them all in.
5 Reheat in a small non-stick saucepan if necessary, stirring all the time. Serve piping hot.

Pan-braised Celery with Satsuma Ⓥ

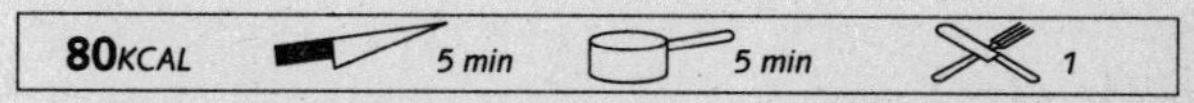

Celery tastes so different when it's cooked. You could serve some grilled steak or gammon with this, some slices of roast chicken or a little grilled fish.

2 sticks celery
½ small onion
1 satsuma or other small thin-skinned orange
½ teaspoon walnut oil

1 Cut the celery into thick slices. Peel and finely chop the onion. Squeeze juice from satsuma.
2 Heat the oil in a non-stick saucepan. Add the celery and onion and fry over a medium heat, stirring all the time, for 2 to 3 minutes.
3 Add the juice from the satsuma and bring to the boil. Cook for 1 minute and serve hot.

Swede, Carrot and Tattie Mash Ⓥ

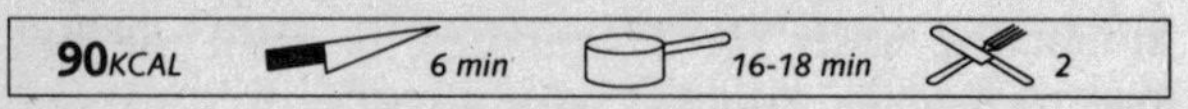

This makes a lovely topping for a cottage pie (see recipe for *Mince with Mushrooms and Garlic* on page 251) or is great served as a main meal with something cheesy or meaty on the side, so I always make a double quantity and cool the rest and store, covered, in the fridge for up to 2 days.

To make the mash into a main meal, pile the mixture into a small heatproof serving dish and top with 25g (1oz) grated cheese. Grill and serve.

125g (4oz) swede
125g (4oz) carrot
125g (4oz) potato
salt
ground black pepper
2 tablespoons chopped fresh chives

1 Thickly peel the swede. Scrape the carrots. Peel the potato. Cut them all into very small chunks so they will cook quickly.
2 Put the swede and the carrot into a small pan and cover with water. Add some salt. Bring to the boil, reduce the heat and simmer for 7 minutes.
3 Add the potatoes and continue cooking for 8 to 10 minutes or until all the vegetables feel soft when they are prodded with a fork. Drain well and return the pan to the heat. Shake the pan over the heat for

30 seconds or so to dry off any extra liquid.
4 Remove from the heat and mash with a potato masher. Season with pepper and stir in the chives.
5 Serve half the mixture piping hot.

Curried Carrots Ⓥ

Whole baby carrots are very tender, very sweet and quick to cook. Try taking a spoon of lime pickle from near the bottom of the jar, avoiding the excess oil on the top, for maximum flavour and minimum calories. Accompany with a plain grilled lamb chop, chicken breast or piece of fish.

175g (6oz) whole baby carrots
1 tablespoon Greek yoghurt
½ teaspoon mild lime pickle
1 teaspoon chopped fresh coriander

1 Trim the roots off the carrots and place in a small non-stick saucepan. Cover with cold water, bring to the boil and simmer for 7 to 10 minutes until the carrots are tender but not soft.
2 Mix the yoghurt and lime pickle together. Drain the carrots, place on a dish and spoon the sauce over the carrots. Scatter the coriander on top. Eat straight away or cool and serve as a salad.

Brussels Sprouts with Lemon and Toasted Breadcrumbs Ⓥ

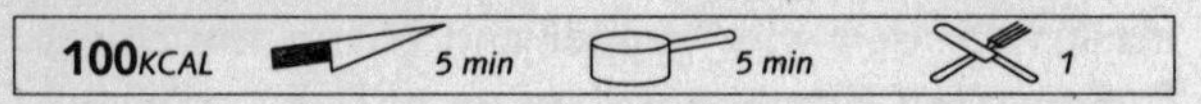

Brussels sprouts were one of those nightmare childhood vegetables, served up soggy, bitter and sludgy for school dinners. Avoid frozen ones and choose the smallest, freshest ones you can find. Boil them lightly and serve them just soft and bright green.

150g (6oz) small Brussels sprouts
15g (½oz) fresh wholemeal bread
1 lemon (for the rind only)

1 Trim the bases off the Brussels sprouts with a sharp knife and mark a cross on the stem. Drop them into a small saucepan.
2 Add 1.5cm (½in) cold water. Bring to the boil, reduce the heat, cover and simmer for 5 minutes.
3 Meanwhile, grate the bread on the coarse side of the grater to make crumbs. Finely grate the rind from the lemon. Mix the breadcrumbs and the lemon rind together and dry fry in a small non-stick frying-pan over a medium heat, stirring all the time until evenly golden.
4 Drain the Brussels sprouts and add to the frying-pan. Stir well until they are coated and pile onto the serving plate. Serve hot.

Red Cabbage and Apple Stir-fry Ⓥ

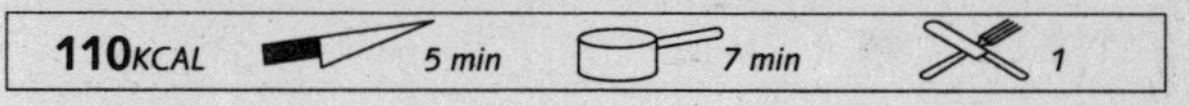

Delicious with grilled chops – especially pork – or a roast chicken or beef casserole. Shredded finely and cooked on the hob, this cabbage and apple mixture makes a quick and colourful vegetable dish.

½ small onion
100g (4oz) red cabbage
1 small sweet eating apple
1 teaspoon unrefined soft brown sugar
1 teaspoon malt vinegar
2 tablespoons unsweetened orange juice
½ teaspoon olive oil

1 Peel and finely chop the onion. Finely shred the red cabbage and cut into short lengths. Peel, core and finely slice the apple.
2 Spoon the sugar, vinegar and orange juice into a small cup. Add 2 tablespoons cold water.
3 Heat the oil in a large non-stick saucepan and fry the onion over a high heat for 1 minute, stirring.
4 Add the cabbage, apple and the orange juice mixture and stir for 1 minute.
5 Reduce the heat, cover and simmer for 5 minutes until the cabbage has softened a little but is still crisp to bite. The juice will have reduced to a thick sauce so that the cabbage is moist but not wet. Stir well to mix and serve hot.

Grilled Tomatoes and Courgettes Ⓥ

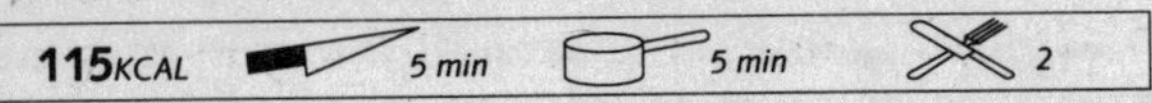

Choose tomatoes and courgettes that are the same size in diameter for the best effect as you will be arranging them in overlapping layers in a serving dish. This dish is attractive and I often cook it if I have a friend round for supper as there is enough for 2 portions, or use the second half cold for lunch. If you are a vegetarian, you could eat both portions with some rice or crusty bread for a main meal. While you've got the grill on you could cook some chicken or fish to serve with the vegetables.

1 large courgette
3 or 4 medium tomatoes
salt
ground black pepper
1 teaspoon fresh thyme leaves
1 teaspoon olive oil
15g (½oz) grated fresh Parmesan cheese

1 Pre-heat the grill to its highest setting. Peel alternate thin strips of skin lengthwise from the courgette to make a pattern. Cut the tomatoes into slices. Cut the courgette into slices the same thickness as the tomatoes.

2 Arrange the tomatoes and courgettes overlapping in a single layer in a flat, shallow, heatproof dish.

3 Season with salt and pepper, scatter thyme leaves

on top. Oil the vegetables using your fingers.
4 Grill for 3 to 4 minutes until the courgettes are beginning to soften. Scatter the Parmesan over and grill for a further 1 minute until golden. Serve hot.

Spinach with Garlic and Apple Ⓥ

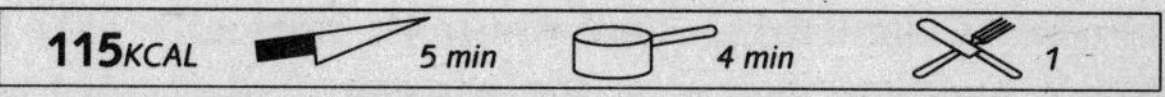

Fresh spinach, served as a vegetable, tastes miles better than frozen. Choose young spinach and cook it only until it has just wilted.

1 clove of garlic
1 small sweet eating apple
100g (4oz) fresh young spinach leaves
½ teaspoon walnut oil

1 Peel and finely slice the garlic. Half fill the sink with water. Add the spinach leaves and swish gently in the water until they are clean. Shake dry. Peel, core and very thinly slice the apple.
2 Heat the oil in a large non-stick pan and fry the garlic and the apple for 1 minute, stirring all the time.
3 Add the spinach leaves, stir well, cover the pan and cook over a medium heat for 3 minutes until the spinach has wilted. Stir well and serve hot.

Quick Cauliflower Cheese Ⓥ

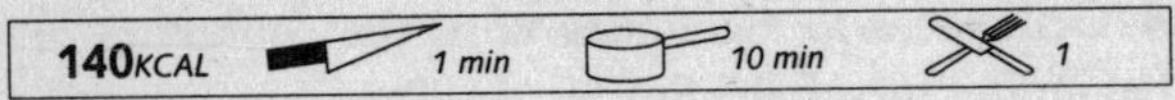

When I was at school, I took a summer holiday job in a hotel kitchen and this was how they made the cauliflower cheese. Everyone used to love it and it was so easy it was almost shameful. If processed cheese is something you wouldn't normally eat, I can assure you that it melts to a runny sauce and is better than 'real' cheese in this dish.

175g (6oz) cauliflower florets
1 square processed cheese slice weighing 25g (1oz)

1 Put the florets in a small pan and add 2.5cm (1in) cold water. Bring to the boil, reduce the heat, cover and simmer for 7 to 8 minutes until the stalks feel tender when you prod them with a knife. Drain.
2 Meanwhile, pre-heat the grill to its highest setting. Arrange the cauliflower in a small heatproof dish. Cover with the cheese slice and grill for 1 minute until the cheese is just melted and beginning to bubble. Serve straight away.

- Exercise helps to tone your muscles which will help to improve the shape of your body. Make regular exercise an enjoyable activity. Don't eat – exercise!

Home-made Oven Chips Ⓥ

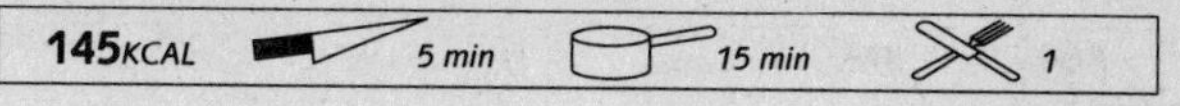

These are a lot easier and safer to make than their deep-fried alternatives and lower in calories too. One potato cut into thick-cut chips will have fewer calories than one potato cut into thin-cut chips. This is because thick-cut chips have a smaller surface area and absorb less oil. No need to peel the potatoes either. Serve hot with plenty of vinegar. (Parsnips are also delicious cooked this way.)

175g (6oz) baking potato
1 teaspoon olive oil
good shake coarse sea salt

1 Pre-heat the oven to its highest setting.
2 Cut the potato into thick chips about 1.5cm (½in) thick. Line a small baking tin with a sheet of foil.
3 Rub half the oil over a small piece of the foil with your fingertips. Add the potatoes and drizzle the rest of the oil over them. Roll the potatoes in the oil so that all the sides are lightly coated.
4 Bake for 7 minutes. Remove the tray from the oven, turn the chips over and put them back in to cook for another 7 minutes or until the chips are crisp and golden on the outside and feel soft when prodded with a sharp knife. Season with salt and serve hot.

Celeriac and Potato Purée with Nutmeg Ⓥ

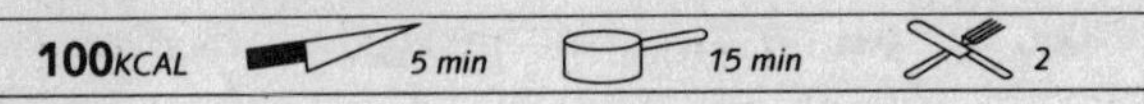

To reduce the number of calories in a spoonful of mash you have to mix the potatoes with something that mashes well but has fewer calories. Celeriac – that knobbly, swollen root vegetable – fits the bill. Potatoes are one of the few things that I add salt to these days but I think they really need it to bring out their flavour.

This recipe is much easier to make in the quantity given and I store the extra portion, covered, in the fridge for up to 2 days. Try it flattened to a thick pancake and dry-fried in a small non-stick frying-pan so that the base goes crispy. Slide onto a serving plate and flip back into the pan to cook the other side. Serve with some grilled lean bacon or a gammon chop and grilled tomatoes.

200g (8oz) baking potato
200g (8oz) celeriac
salt
ground black pepper
⅛ teaspoon ground nutmeg

1 Peel potato and celeriac and cut into small chunks. Place in a small pan and just cover with cold water. Add a little salt.
2 Bring to the boil, reduce the heat, cover and simmer for 14 minutes or until both vegetables feel

soft when prodded with a fork. Drain well and return the pan to the heat. Shake the pan over the heat to drive off any extra liquid.
3 Remove from the heat and mash with a potato masher, season with pepper and nutmeg. Serve half the mixture piping hot, saving the remainder for another day.

Broccoli Stalks with Blue Cheese Ⓥ

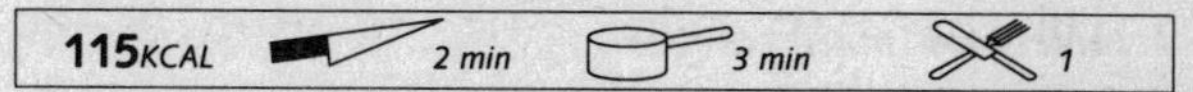

So many people trim broccoli into neat florets and throw away the stalks. What a waste. I cut the stalks into thin slices, steam or boil them and toss with a pungent blue cheese. This recipe makes a great topping for plain pasta or it goes well served with grilled chicken or fish. Brussels sprouts are also delicious cooked this way.

150g (6oz) broccoli stalks
21g (¾oz) cube of Danish blue cheese

1 Slice the broccoli stalks thinly. Place them in a small pan with 1.5cm (½in) water. Bring to the boil, reduce the heat, cover and simmer for 2 minutes. Drain and return to the pan.
2 Add the cheese to the pan. Cover with a lid and heat for 1 minute for the cheese to melt, shaking pan occasionally. Serve hot.

Cauliflower with Sweet-and-sour Sauce Ⓥ

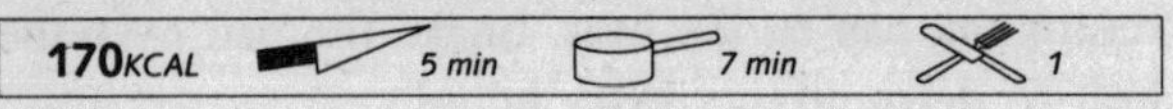

This is an easy, but successful, sauce that gets the balance between sweet, sour and salty just right. Good, too, with stir-fried vegetables and over grilled chicken or fish. Serve with some plain boiled rice or noodles for a main meal.

200g (8oz) cauliflower florets
1 tablespoon malt vinegar
1 tablespoon unrefined soft brown sugar
2 teaspoons tomato purée
2 teaspoons dark soy sauce
125ml (¼pt) unsweetened orange juice
2 teaspoons cornflour

1 Bring a small pan of water to the boil. Drop in the cauliflower, reduce the heat, cover and simmer for 5 minutes until the cauliflower is tender but not soft. Drain and return to the pan.
2 To make the sauce: place the vinegar, sugar, tomato purée, soy sauce and orange juice in a separate small pan. Bring to the boil.
3 Meanwhile mix the cornflour with a little cold water in a cup to form a smooth pouring paste.
4 Pour the cornflour into the boiling sauce, stirring continuously to make a smooth, shiny, and slightly thickened sauce. Boil for 1 minute and then add the cauliflower. Stir well to coat and serve.

Shredded Cabbage with Leek and Orange Ⓥ

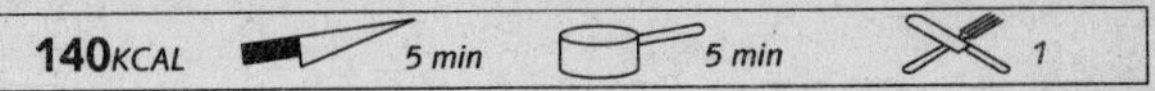

This is much more interesting than the boiled cabbage you may remember from school days which was cold, tough, pale and watery. This cabbage is crisp, green, moist and full of flavour. Grills and roast meats, and plain boiled rice are good accompaniments.

100g (4oz) savoy cabbage or spring greens
1 small leek
1 small orange
½ teaspoon olive oil
black pepper

1 Cut the white core out of the cabbage and shred very finely. Trim the root off the leek, cut in half lengthwise and rinse the leaves thoroughly to wash out any grit. Slice thinly. Finely grate the rind from the orange and squeeze the juice.
2 Heat the oil in a large non-stick saucepan and add the cabbage, leek and orange rind. Stir fry for 1 to 2 minutes.
3 Add the orange juice, reduce the heat, cover and continue to cook for 2 minutes, stirring occasionally. Season with pepper and serve hot.

PASTA AND NOODLES

Pasta is a good-for-you-food.

It's cheap, quick and easy to cook, widely available and easy to store. What usually pushes up the calorie count is the sauce we serve with it and the *amount* of pasta we eat. Forget about eating the sort of platefuls that you would get at your average pasta restaurant. These are easily 3 or 4 times the quantity you need to adjust to when you are counting calories with a view to shifting a few pounds.

A modest 175g (6oz) portion of cooked, plain-boiled pasta will give you 250 calories and would fill a saucer. The trick is to bulk it out with ingredients like vegetables, so that you don't feel the portion is too stingy.

The other thing to watch out for is the sauce you serve with the pasta. Steer clear of creamy sauces and opt instead for anything with a tomato base and good flavours like chillies, black olives, garlic and pungent herbs like basil. Parmesan cheese, although one of the higher calorie cheeses has a concentrated, buttery flavour and, grated, a little goes a long way.

I cook a whole 500g (1lb 2oz) bag of pasta at a time and then freeze it into eight 175g (6oz) portions (the weight of pasta trebles when cooked). If you freeze the pasta in a single layer, wrapped in cling film, it defrosts quickly and evenly. Once frozen, wrap well in more clingfilm, label and date. To defrost, I give it 2 minutes on full power

(100%) in the microwave oven, or plunge it into boiling water and give it a stir. By freezing it in portions, I'm not tempted to overeat as in order to do so would mean a deliberate effort to defrost extra.

All pasta shapes have the same number of calories weight for weight. Fresh pasta is heavier than dried when raw but they are no different from a calorie point of view, weight for weight, once cooked. Both have the same number of calories per portion.

Fusilli with Roasted Peppers and Garlic Ⓥ

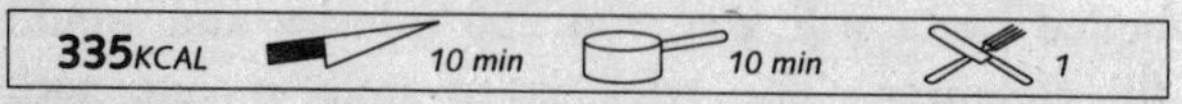

I'm not fond of green peppers so I rarely buy them. But I love the milder, sweeter red and yellow peppers and I think they make a great fresh-tasting sauce for plain boiled pasta or grilled fish. Yellow peppers have twice the calories of red or green peppers though, so to save some calories you could make this sauce with two red peppers or one red and one green.

I use this sauce as a base for lots of different dishes. It tastes much better than anything that you will get out of a jar and the sauce cooks in the same time it takes to boil the pasta. Try adding 25g (1oz) grated Parmesan or Pecorino cheese or stir in 1 teaspoon of drained capers and a tablespoon of fresh chopped parsley to make a Sicilian pepperonata sauce, for a change.

1 red pepper weighing 175g (6oz)
1 yellow pepper weighing 175g (6oz)
1 beef tomato
1 clove of garlic
1 large sprig of fresh oregano
50g (2oz) dried fusilli (pasta spirals)

1 Pre-heat the grill to its highest setting.
2 Halve and deseed the peppers and place, cut-side down, on a non-stick baking sheet. Add the tomato, garlic and oregano to the pan.
3 Grill for 5 to 7 minutes until the peppers are blackened and the skin of the tomato is split.
4 Meanwhile, bring a small pan of water to the boil. Add the pasta spirals and turn the heat down. Half cover and simmer for 6 minutes or until the pasta is soft enough to bite with no chewy bits in the middle, but not so soft that it's soggy. Drain and return to the pan.
5 When the peppers are cooked, remove them from the tray, cut into rough squares and add to the drained pasta.
6 Tip the tomato, garlic, oregano and any juices on the tray into a liquidiser and run the machine until the mixture is runny. Place a sieve over the pan with the pasta and peppers in it and sieve the liquid onto them. Discard the seeds and skin in the sieve.
7 Heat the sauce through, stirring, until the pasta is piping hot. Pile into a serving bowl.

Fusilli with Tomatoes and Herbs Ⓥ

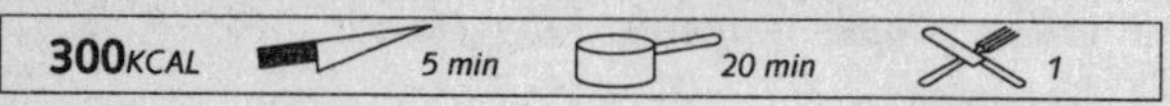

I use this tomato sauce as a base for lots of different pasta meals. Sometimes I add a chopped red chilli with the vegetables at the start of cooking, sometimes some dried tomato halves to give it a more intense tomato flavour or I stir in a teaspoon of pesto to make it more herby.

50g (2oz) dried fusilli
1 small onion
1 clove garlic
1 stick celery
1 red pepper
397g (14oz) can tomatoes with herbs

1 Bring a small pan of water to the boil. Add the fusilli and turn the heat down. Half cover and simmer for 6 minutes or until the pasta is soft enough to bite with no chewy bits in the middle, but not so soft that it's soggy. Drain and set aside.
2 Peel and chop the onion and the garlic. Finely chop the celery. Halve, deseed and finely chop the red pepper.
3 Put the onion, garlic, celery, red pepper and canned tomatoes into a small pan. Bring to the boil, reduce the heat, cover and simmer for 10 minutes.
4 Add the drained pasta to the tomato sauce and stir to mix and warm pasta through. Serve hot.

Penne with Pesto and Sugar Snaps Ⓥ

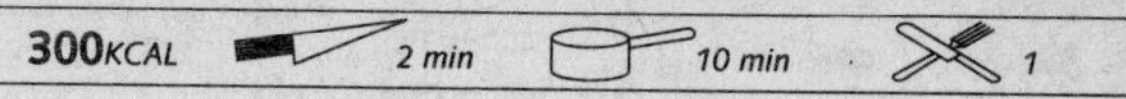

Pesto – a pasta sauce made from fresh basil leaves, pinenuts and fresh Parmesan or Pecorino cheese – is now widely available. If you get the chance, buy it freshly made from an Italian deli. Alternatively, in supermarkets, buy pesto in tubs found with the fresh pasta rather than the sauce in jars. The flavour is better. This dish is also good cold as a salad. It makes a change from sandwiches if you pack it in a tub to take to work. To save time I cook twice as much pasta as I need and use the other half for the *Penne and Ratatouille Bake* (see recipe on page 186).

50g (2oz) dried penne (pasta quills)
175g (6oz) sugar snap peas or mangetout
1 tablespoon fresh pesto

1 Bring a small pan of water to the boil. Add the penne and turn the heat down. Half cover and simmer for 6 minutes.
2 Add the sugar snap peas, return the water to the boil and boil for 2 minutes. The pasta should be soft enough to bite with no chewy bits in the middle, but not so soft that it's soggy. Drain and return to the pan.
3 Stir the pesto into the pasta and stir well to mix. Serve straight away.

Pasta with Creamy Mushroom Sauce Ⓥ

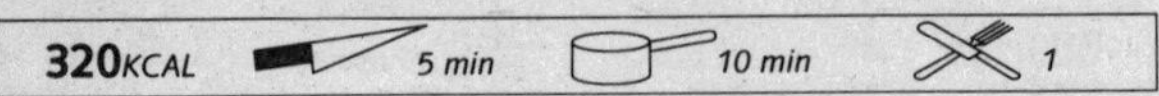

This makes a really mushroomy sauce, full of flavour, yet creamy too. Sometimes I stir in 2 teaspoons of chopped fresh parsley or tarragon if they're handy. The packet soup I use has 60 calories but different brands vary. Check the labels before you buy.

50g (2oz) dried pasta shapes like twists or spirals
125g (4oz) chestnut or brown cap mushrooms
1 teaspoon olive oil
1 packet mushroom cup-a-soup

1 Bring a small pan of water to the boil. Add the pasta and turn the heat down. Half cover and simmer for 6 minutes or until the pasta is soft enough to bite with no chewy bits in the middle, but not so soft that it's soggy. Drain and set aside.
2 Wipe the mushrooms and cut into small pieces. Heat the oil in a small non-stick saucepan and add the mushrooms. Stir-fry for 5 minutes over a very high heat until the mushrooms brown. Set aside.
3 Make up the cup-a-soup with boiling water in a large measuring jug, according to instructions on the pack. Add the fried mushrooms and the pasta and stir well to mix.
4 Return the mixture to the saucepan and bring to the boil. Serve at once.

Spaghetti with Chillies, Black Olives and Garlic Ⓥ

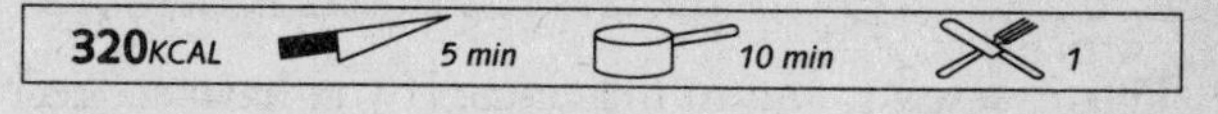

50g (2oz) uncooked spaghetti
1 red chilli
1 clove garlic
10 black olives
1 teaspoon sesame oil
50g (2oz) beansprouts

1 Bring a small pan of water to the boil. Add the pasta and turn the heat down. Half cover and simmer for 6 minutes or until the pasta is soft enough to bite with no chewy bits in the middle, but not so soft that it's soggy. Drain and set aside.
2 Meanwhile, halve the chilli, remove the seeds and cut the flesh into thin slices. Peel the garlic and slice thinly. Halve and stone the olives.
3 Heat the oil in a large, deep-sided, non-stick frying-pan. Add the chilli and garlic and fry for 1 minute until the garlic is golden. Add the beansprouts and cook for 2 minutes, stirring all the time, until they are hot and beginning to wilt.
4 Add the olives and the cooked spaghetti to the pan and stir together until everything is hot. Pile onto a plate and serve straight away.

Penne and Ratatouille Bake Ⓥ

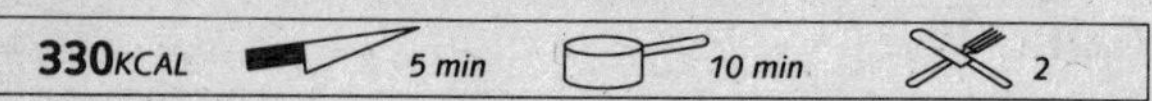

This is so easy, and so delicious. If you have cooked pasta in the freezer and a can of ratatouille in the cupboard, you can rustle this up very speedily. It's a handy dish to cook for unexpected guests too. However, if I'm only cooking for me, I cover the second portion and keep in fridge for up to 3 days. Reheat it in the oven or microwave until piping hot and grill until golden.

50g (2oz) dried penne (pasta quills)
397g (14oz) can ratatouille
4 tablespoons thick Greek yoghurt
15g (½oz) fresh Parmesan

1 Bring a small pan of water to the boil. Add the penne and turn the heat down. Half cover and simmer for 6 minutes or until the pasta is soft enough to bite with no chewy bits in the middle, but not so soft that it's soggy. Drain and return to the pan.
2 Pre-heat the grill to its highest setting.
3 Empty the ratatouille into a small non-stick saucepan and bring to the boil. Add to the penne and stir well to coat.
4 Tip the penne mixture into 2 small ovenproof serving dishes. Spread the yoghurt thinly over the top.

5 Grate the Parmesan and scatter it over the yoghurt. Grill one portion for 1 to 2 minutes until the top is golden and the pasta is heated through. Serve hot.

Tagliatelle with Courgettes, Chicken and Dill

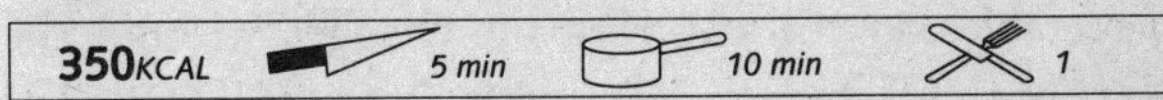

50g (2oz) dried tagliatelli
175g (6oz) baby courgettes
1 small spring onion
25g (1oz) boneless, skinless chicken breast, roasted
7 tablespoons natural yoghurt
2 tablespoons chopped fresh dill

1 Bring a small pan of water to the boil. Add the tagliatelli and turn the heat down. Half cover and simmer for 6 minutes or until the pasta is soft enough to bite with no chewy bits in the middle, but not so soft that it's soggy. Drain and set aside.
2 Dice the courgettes, leaving their skins on. Strip the outer leaf from the spring onion, trim off the root and finely cut both the green and the white parts into rings. Cut the chicken into small cubes.
3 Place the courgettes, spring onions, chicken, fromage frais and dill in a small non-stick saucepan and heat, without boiling, stirring all the time.
4 Add the tagliatelli and stir well to coat. Serve at once.

Stir-fry with Noodles Ⓥ

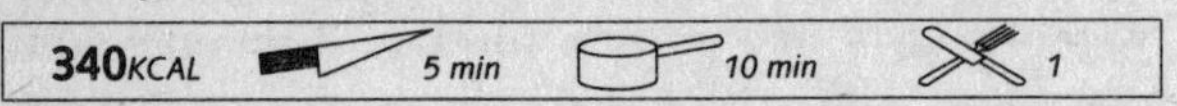

This is a great, no-fuss, basic recipe for when you are hungry. Stir-fry in a few prawns, some cooked chicken or a few slivers of smoked ham if you like. Each supermarket has its own mix of prepared vegetables so you can ring the changes without the expense of being left with lots of half-used vegetables in the bottom of the fridge in order to make this dish.

50g (2oz) dried, medium Chinese egg noodles (about 1 sheet)
1 teaspoon sesame oil
1 pack ready-prepared stir-fry vegetables (with beansprouts, carrots, mushrooms, etc.)
1 teaspoon light soy sauce

1 Bring a kettle of water to the boil. Arrange the noodles in a single layer on the base of a large flat dish. Cover with boiling water and weigh down with something heavy. Leave for 5 minutes. Drain. (Alternatively, follow instructions on the pack.)
2 Heat the sesame oil in a wok or deep-sided, non-stick frying pan. Add the vegetables and stir-fry for 4 to 5 minutes over a high heat, stirring constantly.
3 Add the noodles and continue to fry for a further minute to heat through. Season with soy sauce and serve hot.

Garlic and Sesame Sauce Ⓥ

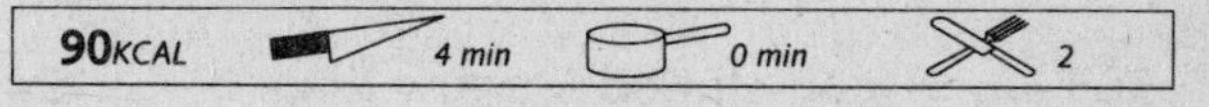

This cold sauce is a wonderful, garlicky, oriental mix which is brilliant spooned onto the *Stir-fry with Noodles* (see recipe on opposite page). It keeps, covered, in the fridge for up to 1 week and can be used to liven up rice, chicken, fish and plain green vegetables too. The list of ingredients is lengthy but everything is easily available and it's quick to mix.

3 cloves garlic
1 small spring onion
2 tablespoons dark soy sauce
1 tablespoons dry sherry
1 teaspoon white wine vinegar
1 teaspoon bought chilli sauce
$\frac{1}{8}$ teaspoon ground black pepper
1 tablespoon smooth peanut butter
1 teaspoon unrefined soft brown sugar
$\frac{1}{2}$ teaspoon sesame oil

1 Peel and crush the garlic into a mixing bowl. Trim the outer leaf from the spring onion, trim off the root and finely chop the green and white parts.
2 Place the garlic and the spring onion in a mixing bowl. Add the soy sauce, dry sherry, vinegar, chilli sauce, black pepper, peanut butter, sugar and sesame oil. Stir well to mix.
3 Spoon over hot noodles, rice or vegetables.

MAIN MEALS – RICE AND GRAINS

Calories	*Recipes*	*Page*
305	Bacon-stuffed Marrow Rings	194
305	Cracked Wheat with Greek Cheese and Olives	202
305	Spanish Rice with Prawns	199
325	Indonesian Rice with Prawns	198
335	Smoked Haddock Kedgeree	195
350	Creamy Mushroom Risotto	192
350	Jambalaya	196
360	Chinese Rice with Green Beans and Cashew Nuts	200

Freeze rice in pre-weighed portions.

Rice, either plain boiled as an accompaniment or mixed in as part of a main meal is a good ingredient to include in your diet. If you can't eat a potato without adding butter, then switch to rice for a change. It's a good basic food that can absorb other flavours easily – warm Indian spices, soy sauce and ginger or tomatoes, chilli and garlic – and is very versatile.

I prefer Basmati rice as it cooks well without going soggy, stays firm and has a good flavour. But there is an increasingly large selection of pre-packed, easy-cook rice in the supermarkets and they are great to ring the changes. Look out for Thai-style rice, the round-grained Italian risotto rice, or long grain rice mixed with the dark grains of wild rice. The only problem with rice is that often the cooking time on the packet is too long and you end up with rice that is soft. My advice is to cook it for half the time it says on the packet and then test it. Keep trying it until you get the right amount of bite left in the rice. Drain and rinse well under hot running water.

So that it is always on hand, I cook a whole 500g (3lb) bag of rice at a time and then freeze it in eight 175g (6oz) portions (the weight of rice trebles when cooked). If you freeze rice in a single layer, it defrosts quickly and evenly. Once frozen, wrap well in clingfilm, label and date. To defrost, I give it 2 minutes on full power (100%) in the microwave oven, or plunge it into boiling water, bring the water back to the boil and stir. The ready-weighed portions are useful for speedy suppers and to avoid the temptation of helping yourself to seconds...

Creamy Mushroom Risotto Ⓥ

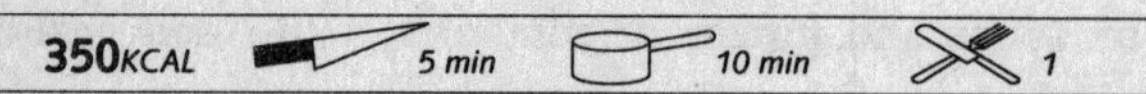

This is a really sensational dish. Risotto is one of my favourite things to eat and a very satisfying dish to cook. You need to stand and stir it, adding stock a little at a time, until the rice absorbs the stock but stays creamy. If you are likely to nibble in the kitchen, pour yourself a large glass of iced water to sip or prepare a bowl of carrot and celery sticks or raw mangetout and nibble these while you are cooking. Buy a tub of fresh chicken or vegetable stock for the best result, and try to use chestnut mushrooms as they have bags more flavour than button mushrooms yet have the same firm texture. Although you only need a tablespoonful, the red wine does add a lovely flavour. Buy wine in a can or a half-bottle and enjoy a glass with the risotto. Serve with a crisp green salad for a stylish supper. When I was testing this recipe for the book, my family thought it was so good that we ate it for supper four nights in a row.

1 small onion
175g (6oz) chestnut (sometimes called brown cap) mushrooms
1 teaspoon olive oil
50g (2oz) Arborio (risotto) rice
1 tablespoon dry white wine
250ml (½pt) fresh chicken stock
salt
ground black pepper
15g (½oz) fresh Parmesan

1 Peel and finely chop the onion. Wipe and slice the mushrooms.
2 Heat the oil in a small non-stick saucepan. Add the onion and the rice and stir for 1 minute so that the rice is well coated and the onion is shiny.
3 Add the wine and allow it to bubble away. Add the mushrooms and a third of the stock and stir the mixture constantly, but gently, until the mixture just begins to stick to the pan.
4 Add a third more stock and continue stirring until it is absorbed. Add half the remaining stock. (Taste the rice as you may not need all the stock – it depends on how quickly the rice cooks.) The rice is cooked when it is tender all the way through but is still saucy and looks like a creamy rice pudding.
5 Season with salt, if needed, and pepper and grate fresh Parmesan over the top. Serve hot.

Bacon-stuffed Marrow Rings

A ring of marrow makes a good nest for this savoury rice filling. You can cook the rest of the marrow for another meal by steaming it or frying it in a little oil then tossing it in grated lemon rind and ground black pepper. This quantity of filling will also fill one small green or red pepper or a couple of large flat mushrooms.

25g (1oz) leek
25g (1oz) smoked back bacon
1 teaspoon olive oil
150g (5oz) cooked, mixed, long grain rice with wild rice
1 teaspoon fresh thyme leaves
1 teaspoon chopped fresh parsley
2 slices of marrow 2.5cm (1in) thick
1 slice of processed cheese

1 Pre-heat the oven to its highest setting.Trim and slice the leek lengthwise, rinse thoroughly and chop. Remove any fat from the bacon and cut into small pieces using scissors.
2 Heat the oil in a small non-stick frying-pan and fry the leek and the bacon over a medium heat for 1 minute until the bacon is golden. Add the rice, thyme and parsley and stir well to mix. Take the pan off the heat.

3 Cut out the seeds and the soft spongy centres of the marrow pieces using a sharp knife. Place the marrow rings in an ovenproof serving dish and spoon the rice mixture over the top. Pour a little water around the marrow to come half-way up the sides and place cheese over top. Cover the dish with foil.
4 Bake for 15 to 20 minutes until the marrow is tender when you prod it with a knife. Serve hot.

Smoked Haddock Kedgeree

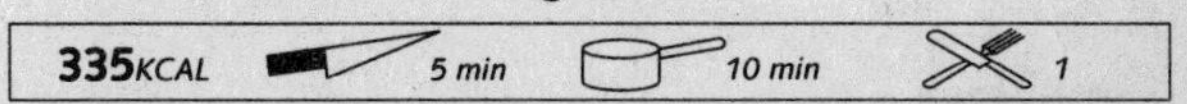

If you can buy it from a reliable source, a piece of fresh smoked haddock is a joy. Look for the pale, naturally smoked vaiety for the purest and rarest flavour (although I was brought up on the dyed sort. Any smoked fish – be it cod or haddock – we affectionately still call 'yellow' fish). If you can't buy it fresh, it's very good pre-packd and frozen.

1 small onion
½ teaspoon olive oil
1 teaspoon curry powder
50g (2oz) long grain rice
250ml (½pt) vegetable stock
50g (2oz) skinless smoked haddock fillet

Smoked Haddock Kedgeree continued

1 Peel and finely chop the onion.

2 Heat the oil in a small non-stick pan. Add the onion, curry powder and rice and fry for 1 minute until the rice and the onion are shiny.

3 Add the stock. Bring to the boil, reduce the heat, cover and simmer for 7 minutes. Add the haddock and cook for a further 3 minutes or until the rice feels tender and the stock is absorbed.

4 When cooked, stir well to flake the fish. Serve straight away.

Jambalaya

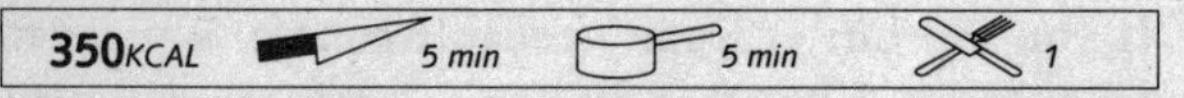

Jambalaya is one of the star recipes of Cajun cooking in the deep south of America where many of the recipes have a 'holy trinity' of ingredients – green pepper, spring onions and celery. Try making this with chicken breast instead of the pork fillet for a change and look out for Cajun seasoning – a ready-made mix of herbs and spices which usually includes oregano, garlic and paprika. A shake of that instead of pepper adds a lovely flavour.

1 large tomato
2 spring onions
1 stick green celery
½ green pepper
50g (2oz) pork fillet
1 teaspoon olive oil
175g (6oz) cooked, long grain white rice
ground black pepper
dash Tabasco hot pepper sauce
1 tablespoon chopped fresh parsley

1 Skin and chop the tomato. Trim and finely chop the spring onions. Dice the celery into small pieces. Deseed and core the pepper. Trim any fat and shiny white bits from the pork and cut into small cubes.
2 Heat the oil in a small non-stick frying-pan. Add the spring onion, celery, green pepper and pork and fry for 1 minute, stirring the mixture to brown the pork.
3 Add the tomatoes and rice and stir for 5 minutes until heated through and vegetables are softened.
4 Season with black pepper, a dash of Tabasco to taste and sprinkle with parsley. Serve straight away.

• No pain, no gain is nonsense. If exercise hurts, you are pushing yourself too hard (or not doing it properly). Take it slowly and enjoy it. You have to keep it up for the rest of your life.

Indonesian Rice with Prawns

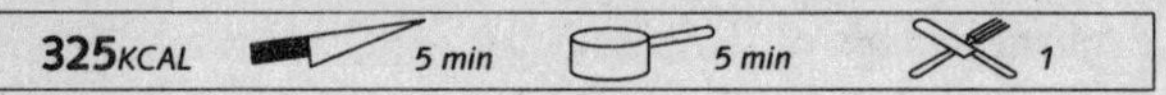

Inspired by a couple of Christmas holidays spent with my sister and her husband in Singapore, this mildly spiced rice dish is one of our favourites. It's good served with cooling fingers of cucumber, or a plate of cucumber salad and some crisp strips of red pepper. If you have any to hand, a sprinkling of chopped fresh coriander is lovely over the top. The flavour is very subtle and even if the ingredients list looks long, it is quick to throw together.

1 fresh red chilli
1 spring onion
1 clove of garlic
25g (1oz) lean cooked ham
1 teaspoon vegetable oil
½ teaspoon ground coriander
1 teaspoon dark soy sauce
½ teaspoon soft brown sugar
¼ teaspoon anchovy essence
100g (4oz) cooked rice (made from 40g (1½oz) uncooked rice boiled in water)
50g (2oz) cooked peeled prawns

1 Deseed the chilli and finely chop. Strip the outer leaf from the spring onion, trim off the root and finely chop both the green and white parts. Peel and finely chop the garlic. Chop the ham finely.

2 Heat the oil in a small pan. Add the chilli, spring onion, garlic and ham and fry for 2 minutes, over a medium heat, until the mixture is golden.
3 Mix the ground coriander, soy sauce, sugar and anchovy essence in a cup and stir well. Add to the ham mixture and allow it to simmer.
4 Add the rice and prawns and stir-fry for 1 to 2 minutes to heat through. Serve hot.

Spanish Rice with Prawns

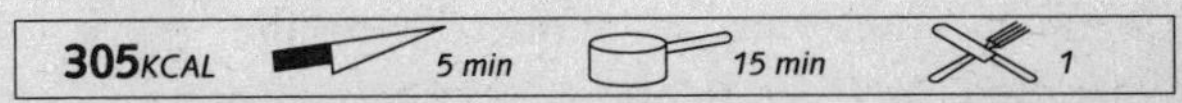

The ingredients list looks long but this dish is quick to make and is really delicious. If you have saffron threads, do add the tiniest pinch. They will colour the rice a pale yellow and add an authentic scent.

1 small onion
1 clove garlic
1 teaspoon olive oil
50g (2oz) long grain rice
50g (2oz) boneless, skinless chicken breast
200ml (7fl oz) half-strength chicken stock made from a cube
pinch saffron threads (optional)
½ red pepper
1 stick celery
50g (2oz) cooked, peeled prawns
1 tablespoon chopped fresh parsley

Spanish Prawns with Rice continued

1 Peel and finely chop the onion. Peel and crush the garlic

2 Heat the oil in a non-stick saucepan, add the onion, garlic, rice and chicken and fry for 1 to 2 minutes until all the oil is absorbed.

3 Add the stock, bring to the boil, reduce the heat, cover and simmer for 10 minutes, without lifting the lid, until most of the stock is absorbed.

4 While the rice is cooking, deseed and chop the pepper. Finely dice the celery.

5 When the rice is tender and the stock is absorbed, add the peppers, celery and prawns. Stir well to mix, cover and cook for a further 2 minutes until heated through. Stir well, scatter the parsley on top and serve hot.

Chinese Rice with Green Beans and Cashew Nuts Ⓥ

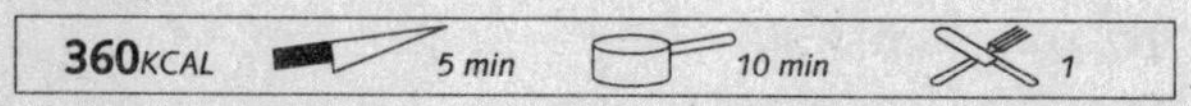

This is a crisp, colourful rice dish which is full of fresh flavours. The water chestnuts that you don't use can be tipped into a bowl, covered and kept in the fridge for up to 3 days. Use them to add crunch to salads, stuffings and sandwich fillings. Drain the rice well and make sure you use a non-stick pan for frying otherwise you'll use too much oil.

50g (2oz) long grain white rice
50g (2oz) fresh green beans
1 clove of garlic
1 spring onion
6mm (¼ in) slice of fresh ginger root
½ red pepper
5 canned water chestnuts weighing 25g (1oz), drained
½ teaspoon sesame oil
15g (½oz) salted cashew nuts
½ teaspoon dark soy sauce

1 Bring a pan of water to the boil. Add the rice, half cover and simmer for 5 minutes only.
2 Meanwhile, trim the green beans and cut them into short lengths. Peel and slice the garlic. Trim and chop the spring onion. Peel and finely chop the ginger. Deseed and core the red pepper. Cut into strips and then into diamond-shaped pieces. Slice the water chestnuts.
3 After the rice has cooked for 5 minutes, add the beans, return to the boil and cook for 2 minutes only. Drain and rinse under hot running water.
4 Heat the oil in a large non-stick frying-pan. Add the garlic, spring onion, ginger, red pepper, water chestnuts and cashew nuts and stir-fry for 2 minutes. Add the rice and beans and stir well over the heat for a further minute. Season with soy sauce and serve straight away or allow to cool to room temperature and serve as a salad.

Cracked Wheat with Greek Cheese and Olives Ⓥ

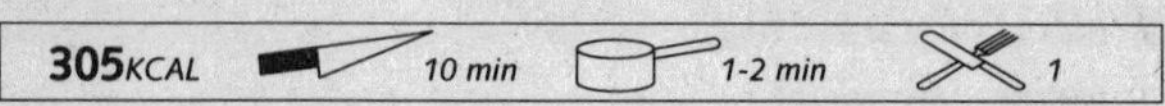

Cracked wheat is a wonderful ingredient. It's easy to find in any supermarket and very easy to cook. You just add boiling water and it puffs up to a slightly chewy grain which makes a change from rice and makes a good base for a salad. Haloumi cheese is a firm, waxy, salty Greek cheese which is good grilled, and is firm enough to be cut into cubes, threaded onto skewers and grilled for a vegetarian kebab. Use Gruyère, a flavoured Edam or a mature Gouda instead of Haloumi if you like.

6 tablespoons boiling water
1 teaspoon olive oil
1 teaspoon fresh lemon or lime juice
1 teaspoon chopped fresh mint
40g (1½oz) cracked wheat
1 large beef tomato weighing about 175g (6oz)
1 spring onion
4 stoned black olives
25g (1oz) Haloumi cheese

1 Measure the boiling water, oil, lemon or lime juice and mint into a large bowl. Add the cracked wheat, stir well, cover with a plate and leave to stand for 10 minutes.
2 Meanwhile, put the tomato into a small heatproof

bowl, cover with boiling water and leave for 30 seconds until its skin splits when you prod it with a knife. Drain off the water and skin and chop the tomato. Trim and finely chop the spring onion. Quarter the olives. Cut the cheese into small cubes.

3 Add the tomato, spring onion, olives and cheese to the wheat mixture and stir well. Serve as it is or pile the mixture into a small non-stick pan and stir over a medium heat for 1 to 2 minutes to heat through. Eat straight away.

- Choose an exercise which:
  - You can enjoy
  - Makes you feel good
  - You can do regularly for 20 or 30 minutes, two or three times a week
  - You can fit into your everyday routine
  - You can do near home
  - Doesn't depend on the weather or the season
  - Suits your level of fitness.

MAIN MEALS – EGGS

All the fat of an egg is in the yolk.

A couple of eggs make a quick and calorie friendly supper, but aim to have no more than 4 a week. Eggs are relatively high in cholesterol and doctors recommend that we keep our cholesterol levels low. All the fat of an egg (and therefore the cholesterol and most of the calories) is in the yolk. Cooked in different ways they taste quite different – try oven-baking them with peppers and tomatoes, scrambling or whisking them into an omelette. Because of the small risk of salmonella poisoning from eggs, the Government recommends that lightly cooked or raw eggs should not be eaten by children, pregnant women, the elderly or people recovering from illness. Hard-boiled eggs are okay.

Eggs keep well stored in the fridge for a couple of weeks. Buy them fresh from a shop with a quick turnover and use them quickly. Look out for those stamped with the date they were laid – useful if you decant them from their box into the door of the fridge.

To test if an egg is fresh, put it in a clear jug filled with cold water. If it lies flat on the bottom, it is very fresh. If it stands upright but still touching the bottom, it is probably a week old but still all right to eat. If it floats to the top, it is old – throw it out.

Mediterranean Omelette Ⓥ

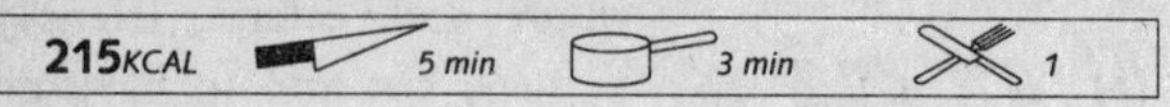

This is a lovely, moist, fresh-tasting omelette full of the flavours of the south of France. Serve it with a crisp green salad of iceberg lettuce tossed with lightly cooked green beans and a dressing flavoured with chopped fresh parsley and capers.

2 tomatoes
6 fresh basil leaves
3 stoned black olives
2 eggs, size 3
ground black pepper
½ teaspoon olive oil

1 Pre-heat the grill to its highest setting. Put the tomatoes in a small heatproof bowl. Cover with boiling water and leave for 30 seconds until their skins split when you prod them with a knife. Drain off the water; skin and chop the tomatoes.
2 Make a stack of basil leaves and shred finely. Coarsely chop the olives.
3 Drain the anchovies of their oil, rinse under cold water and pat dry on kitchen paper. Snip into small pieces with scissors.
4 Crack the eggs into a small bowl. Add 1 tablespoon of water and season with pepper. Beat well with a fork.
5 Heat the oil in a small non-stick omelette pan

over a medium heat and add the egg mixture. Stir gently with a fork.

6 Add the tomato, basil, olives and anchovies and stir into the runny egg mixture. When just set on the base, put the pan under the pre-heated grill, taking care not to heat the handle, and grill the omelette until puffy and lightly golden.

7 Slip onto a serving plate and eat while still piping hot.

Summer Salad Omelette Roll Ⓥ

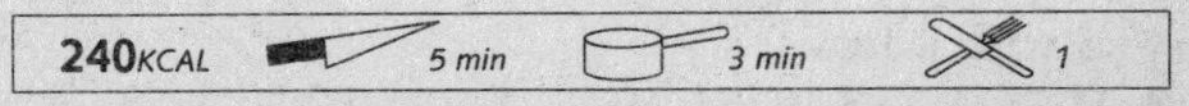

This is one of those recipes where the ingredients mixed together taste much better than the same ingredients served separately. You make it in a large non-stick frying-pan so that the omelette is as thin as a crèpe, then fill it and roll it up Swiss-roll fashion. It makes a great summer evening supper.

2 tomatoes
2.5cm (1in) piece of cucumber
1 small spring onion
1 slice of iceberg lettuce
1 tablespoon chopped fresh parsley
squeeze of fresh lemon juice
½ teaspoon olive oil
2 eggs, size 3
ground black pepper

Summer Salad Omelette Roll continued

1 Pre-heat the grill to its highest setting. Put the tomatoes in a small heatproof bowl. Cover with boiling water and leave for 30 seconds until their skins split when you prod them with a knife. Drain off the water; skin and chop the tomatoes.

2 Finely dice the cucumber. Trim and finely chop the spring onion. Finely shred the lettuce. Mix the tomatoes, cucumber, spring onion, lettuce, parsley and lemon juice together and put to one side.

3 Crack the eggs into a small bowl. Add 1 tablespoon of water and season with pepper. Beat well with a fork.

4 Heat the oil in a large non-stick frying-pan over a medium heat and add the egg mixture. Stir gently with a fork.

5 Scatter the salad mixture over the top and spread it evenly, right to the edges.

6 Put the pan under the pre-heated grill, taking care not to heat the handle, and grill until just set.

7 Lift one edge of the omelette up with a palette knife and roll the omelette and filling up like a Swiss roll. Slip onto a serving plate and cut into about 8 thick slices with a sharp knife. Eat straight away.

Quick Spanish Omelette Ⓥ

Unlike a traditional omelette which should be set on the outside and runny in the middle, a Spanish omelette should be firm enough to pick up in chunks. This is also good served cold and makes a change from sandwiches in a packed lunch.

175g (6oz) frozen special mixed vegetables (peas, beans, carrots and mixed peppers)
2 eggs, size 3
ground black pepper
50g (2oz) boiled or baked potato
1 teaspoon olive oil

1 Bring a small pan of water to the boil. Add the vegetables, return to the boil, reduce the heat, cover and simmer for 3 minutes. Drain.
2 Crack the eggs into a bowl. Add pepper and beat with a fork. Dice potato into small pieces.
3 Pre-heat the grill to its highest setting. Heat the oil in a small non-stick omelette pan. Add the potato and fry for 1 to 2 minutes to brown.
4 Add the vegetables and the egg mixture and cook over a medium heat, stirring gently with a fork.
5 When set, put the pan under the pre-heated grill, until puffy and lightly golden.
6 Slip onto a serving plate and eat while still hot or cool and serve at room temperature.

Japanese Omelette

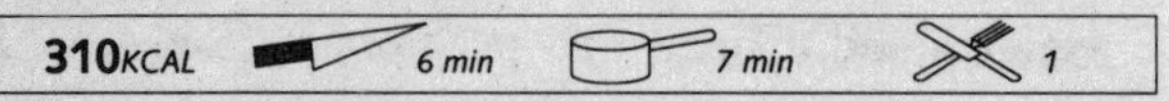

My friend Mitzie went on an eating trip to Japan and came back raving about this recipe which she had eaten out there. I thought she was pulling my leg when she said it was a sort of cabbage omelette with brown sauce on top. However, she cooked it for me and, against all the odds, I had to agree it is a delicious combination. I sometimes cook it on a Monday if we have had roast chicken at the weekend and there are some leftovers. Here's my version.

2 spring onions
50g (2oz) spring cabbage
1 thin slice fresh root ginger
25g (1oz) cooked chicken
25g (1oz) cooked peeled prawns
½ teaspoon sesame oil
2 eggs, size 3
ground black pepper
1 teaspoon dark soy sauce
1 teaspoon brown sauce
pinch unrefined soft brown sugar

1 Trim and finely chop the spring onions. Finely shred the spring cabbage. Peel and finely slice the ginger.
2 Cut the chicken into small chunks, then mix with

the prawns. Put to one side.

3 Heat the oil a small non-stick omelette pan over a medium heat. Add the spring onions, cabbage and ginger and fry for 2 minutes until the cabbage softens a little. Add the chicken and prawns and cook for a further 2 minutes to heat through.

4 Crack the eggs into a small bowl. Add 1 tablespoon of water and season with pepper. Beat well with a fork.

5 Pour the egg mixture into the pan and stir gently with a fork until the base is just set.

6 Put the pan under the pre-heated grill, taking care not to heat the handle, and grill until the top is puffy and lightly golden.

7 Meanwhile, mix the soy sauce, brown sauce and sugar together for the topping. Pour over the top of the omelette and slip it onto a serving plate. Eat while still piping hot.

• It's the food that you eat most of the week that will decide whether you are fat or not. You can't come to too much harm if one meal out of 21 is higher in calories than the rest of the food you enjoy. It is possible to treat yourself.

Scrambled Egg with Trout and Chives

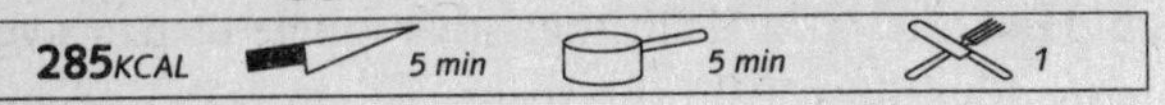

This dish makes a lovely Sunday brunch or a special supper. The smoked trout I use is the thinly sliced see-through sort that looks like smoked salmon. It's a little bit cheaper than the salmon, although the two are interchangeable.

small bunch fresh chives
25g (1oz) smoked trout
2 eggs, size 3
1 tablespoon semi-skimmed milk
ground black pepper
8g (¼oz) butter
1 thin slice wholemeal bread weighing 25g (1oz)

1 Finely snip the chives with scissors into a mixing bowl. Snip the trout into thin pieces and add.
2 Crack in the eggs and spoon in the milk. Add a grinding of pepper. Beat well with a fork to mix.
3 Put the bread in the toaster to toast.
4 Melt the butter in a small non-stick saucepan. Pour in the egg and trout mixture and cook over a low heat, stirring occasionally with a wooden spoon.
5 When the base starts to set, remove from the heat and continue gently scraping the cooked mixture off the base as it sets to scramble it.
6 When the mixture is the consistency you like and still creamy, pile it onto the toast. Eat at once.

Egg MacMuffin

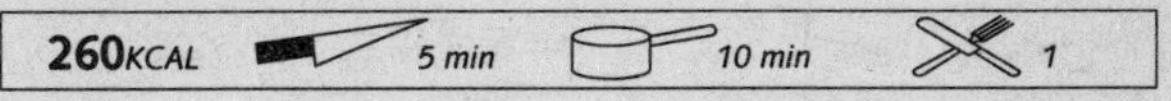

Inspired by a famous American burger chain, this is my calorie-counted version of a savoury muffin. Serve with an interesting, crispy green salad and eat while it's still hot with the cheese drippy and the egg yolk runny. Have some fruit to follow.

1 egg, size 3
bottom half of a soft roll or muffin weighing 25g (1oz)
25g (1oz) slice lean smoked ham
1 processed cheese slice

1 Bring a small pan of water to the boil. Crack in the egg, return the water to the boil, then immediately take the pan off the heat. Set the timer for 3 minutes and cover the pan with a lid.
2 Pre-heat the grill to its highest setting. Place the roll under the grill to warm through. Top with the ham and pop back under the grill.
3 As soon as the timer goes, lift the poached egg out of the water using a slotted spoon. Shake well, to drain off any extra water and arrange the egg on the ham.
4 Top with the cheese slice and return to the grill until the cheese is just bubbling and melted. Serve straight away.

Curried Eggs Ⓥ

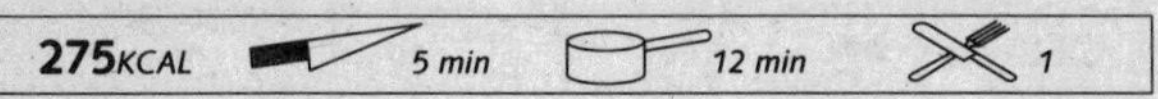

I find this sauce very useful for all sorts of quick curries – and use it with cooked chicken breast, cubes of fish or paneer (a pressed Indian cheese now sold in large supermarkets). Serve with a little plain boiled rice with some peas and spring onions mixed through it.

2 eggs, size 3
1 small onion
1 teaspoon vegetable oil
1 teaspoon mild curry paste
1 teaspoon curry powder
1 teaspoon plain flour
2 teaspoons mango chutney
150ml (¼pt) vegetable stock or water
196g (7oz) canned chopped tomatoes
2 tablespoons thick Greek yoghurt

1 Put the eggs into a small saucepan and cover with cold water. Bring to the boil, reduce the heat so that the water is simmering, cover with a heatproof serving plate and set the timer for 6 minutes.
2 Meanwhile, peel and chop the onion. Heat the oil in a small non-stick saucepan and add the onion, curry paste, curry powder and plain flour and cook for 1 minute, stirring all the time. Add the chutney,

the stock or water and the tomatoes and bring to the boil, stirring. Reduce the heat to a simmer.

3 When the timer goes off, run the eggs under cold water, shell and rinse. Halve and arrange on a warmed serving plate.

4 Stir the yoghurt into the sauce, mix well and sieve over the eggs. Eat straight away.

Baked Egg with Peppers and Tomatoes Ⓥ

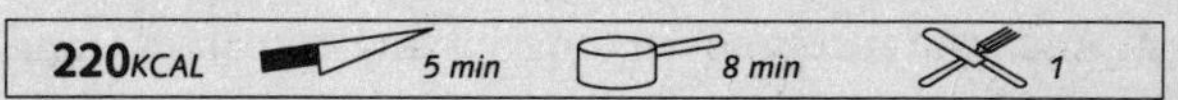

This is a quick and colourful supper dish where you soften the vegetables in a little non-stick frying-pan, crack in an egg and then grill it until the egg sets. Sometimes I add 15g (½oz) of grated Parmesan, Gruyère or Mozzarella before grilling it. Serve with some crusty bread, unbuttered of course.

1 small thin courgette
½ red pepper
½ small onion
1 clove of garlic
1 teaspoon olive oil
1 teaspoon chopped fresh oregano or marjoram
196g (7oz) can chopped tomatoes
ground black pepper
1 egg, size 3

Baked Egg with Peppers and Tomatoes continued

1 Pre-heat the grill to its highest setting. Trim and thinly slice the courgette. Cut out the core and seeds from the pepper and cut into small squares. Peel and slice the onion and the garlic.

2 Heat the oil in a small non-stick frying-pan. Add the courgette, peppers, onion and garlic and cook over a medium heat for 2 to 3 minutes, stirring all the time until the onion is softened and browned.

3 Add the oregano or marjoram, tomatoes, and some black pepper and simmer for 2 minutes. Take the pan off the heat, make a well in the centre and crack in the egg. Scoop some of the hot tomato juice over the top of the egg and place under the pre-heated grill for 2 to 3 minutes until the white has set and the yolk has heated through.

4 Slide the mixture onto a serving plate and eat straight away.

- Remember these four golden rules to enjoying exercise:
  - Get moving
  - Build up gradually
  - Do it regularly
  - Keep doing it.

French Toasts with Basil, Parmesan and Tomatoes Ⓥ

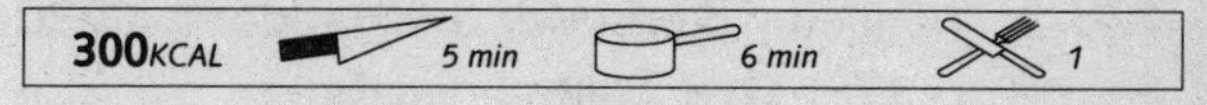

3 ripe plum tomatoes
ground black pepper
15g (½oz) fresh Parmesan
1 egg, size 3
2 teaspoons finely shredded fresh basil
4g (⅛oz) butter
25g (1oz) thick-cut fresh white bread, weighed with the crusts cut off

1 Thickly slice the tomatoes. Top with a good grinding of black pepper.
2 Finely grate the Parmesan cheese into a shallow dish. Add the egg, basil and 1 tablespoon of water and beat well to mix.
3 Press one side of the bread into the egg mixture then turn over and soak the other side.
4 Heat the butter in a small non-stick frying-pan. When it's foamy, add the bread and cook for 1 minute over a medium heat until the base is golden.
5 Turn over and cook the over side. Slide onto a serving plate and keep warm.
6 Add the tomatoes to the hot pan and cook the tomatoes for 1 to 2 minutes over a medium heat, shaking the pan from time to time, until warmed through and softened. Slide onto the toast on the serving plate and eat straight away.

MAIN MEALS – FISH

Eat fish at least once a week.

Fresh or frozen, fish is something that we could all do with eating more of. It often comes in single servings, ready-prepared with no bones or skin and needs only the lightest of cooking. It's a low fat food and so it's lighter on calories than cheeses or red meats. Whichever fish you choose, avoid anything that is deep-fried or coated in batter. Grill, bake or stir-fry fish and try eating it twice a week as a main meal, and have it several times for light meals, too.

If you are lucky enough to have a fresh fish shop near you then use it. Make friends with your fishmonger and get all the preparation done for you in the shop to save you time when you get home. Firm white favourites like fillets of cod and haddock, the flatties like sole and plaice and the pinks like salmon and trout have few bones and are full of flavour. Fish freezes well, too, so you can batch buy when the quality or the price is right and freeze it the same day when you get home.

Of all the oily fish I think smoked mackerel, especially the sort with a crust of black peppercorns, is a good buy and although slightly higher in calories, it does have a stronger flavour so you'll find you eat less. But if you can cope with the bones, herrings, kippers and fresh sardines contain the good-for-you oils that doctors recommend and we'd all be wise to make a point of eating them at least once a week.

Shellfish is a good low-calorie choice but I think of it as a treat for a special occasion, mainly because prawns are costly and mussels are time consuming to prepare. Frozen prawns, though, are not prohibitive and you get quite a lot for your calories. Canned fish is also great to use although I use it mainly with baked potatoes, in sandwiches and on toast (see the appropriate chapters for ideas).

Roasted Cod with Tartare Sauce and Mushy Peas

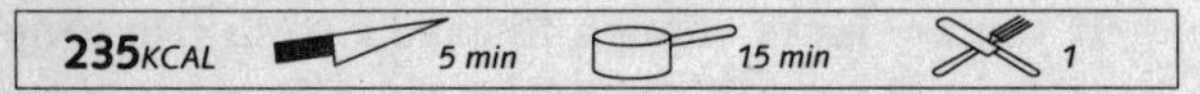

I first tasted *Mushy Peas* in Yorkshire, in Harry Ramsden's excellent fish restaurant. We had cod, chips and mushy peas and a cup of tea, with bread and butter. It was one of those meals you look back on nostalgically and remember it being the best thing you'd ever eaten. (We'd also had lunch at Betty's tearooms in Harrogate so it was a very memorable eating day altogether!). The mushy peas in this dish make a moist sauce for the cod and the whole dish is a meal in itself. You could swap the home-made tartare sauce for 3 tablespoons of shop-bought sauce if you were in a real hurry. If it's a Friday night, I might push the boat out and cook some *Home-made Oven Chips* (see recipe on page 173) to go with this dish.

100g (4oz) canned mushy peas
100g (4oz) fresh, skinless, cod fillet
3 stoned black olives
1 teaspoon capers, drained
1 small pickled gherkin or cornichon, drained
small bunch fresh parsley (enough to make 1 tablespoon when chopped)
1 tablespoon reduced fat mayonnaise
1 tablespoon Greek yoghurt
malt vinegar (optional)

1 Pre-heat the oven to its highest setting. Spoon the mushy peas into a small, single serving, ovenproof dish and mash with a fork.
2 Arrange the cod fillet over peas.
3 Finely chop the olives, capers, gherkin or cornichon and the parsley. Scoop into a small bowl. Add the mayonnaise and the yoghurt to them and mix well.
4 Spoon the sauce over the cod to cover it completely. Arrange a strip of foil round the edge of the dish to cover the peas but leave the cod and the sauce uncovered.
5 Bake for 15 minutes until the cod flakes easily when pressed with a fork and the topping is beginning to go golden. Serve piping hot. Sprinkle some malt vinegar over the mushy peas if you like.

Monkfish and New Potato Kebabs

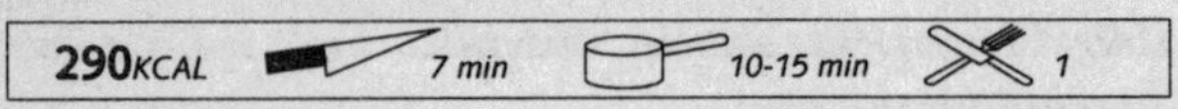

Monkfish is a great fish. It has one main bone that runs the length of its tail and no fiddly little bones coming off this. It is usually sold ready filleted so there's nothing to do at home except dice it and bake it. The very firm and meaty texture is ideal for kebabs because it won't flake off the stick or the skewer. Serve with a salad of sliced tomatoes, lightly grilled on an ovenproof serving plate.

6 small, even-sized, new potatoes together weighing 150g (6oz)
75g (3oz) piece of skinless monkfish fillet
1 small courgette
1 small red pepper
1 tablespoon fresh pesto

1 Scrub the potatoes and place in a small saucepan. Cover with cold water, bring to the boil, reduce the heat and simmer for 6 to 8 minutes or until tender when you prod them with a knife.
2 Meanwhile, cut the monkfish and the courgette into 6 evenly sized pieces. Halve the pepper, deseed and cut each half into 3 pieces.
3 Place the pesto in a mixing bowl. Add 1 tablespoon of water and mix together. Add the monkfish and courgette and mix well. When the potatoes are cooked, drain them and add these too.

4 Pre-heat the grill to its highest setting. Thread the potatoes, monkfish, courgette and red pepper alternately onto 2 skewers.

5 Grill for 2 to 3 minutes and turn. Grill for a further 2 to 3 minutes. Brush with the pesto mixture from the mixing bowl and when the courgette is blistered and the monkfish is cooked through, serve hot.

Trout with Ginger, Chilli and Lime

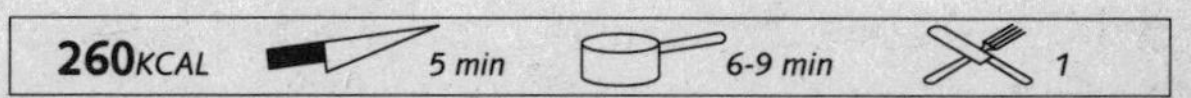

This is a mix-it-and-grill-it recipe, with a sticky glaze on the trout. Thread the vegetables onto skewers and grill at the same time as the fish. I keep a bottle of fresh lime juice in the fridge. It's made from concentrated limes and it's ideal for splashing into marinades if there's not a fresh lime in the fruit bowl.

1 tablespoon ginger marmalade
1 teaspoon sweet chilli sauce
1 teaspoon lime juice
100g (4oz) fresh trout fillet
½ green pepper
1 small courgette
½ teaspoon oil

Trout with Ginger, Chilli and Lime continued

1 Spoon the ginger marmalade, chilli sauce and lime juice into a small bowl and stir to mix.

2 Line a baking tin with foil and add the trout fillet, skin side down. Spoon the glaze over the top.

3 Pre-heat the grill to its highest setting.

4 Deseed the pepper and cut into small squares. Cut the courgette into 1.5cm (½in) chunks. Thread the peppers and courgettes onto 2 skewers. Arrange on a separate baking tin and brush the vegetables lightly with the oil.

5 Place the vegetables under the grill and cook for 2 to 3 minutes on each side. Add the trout to vegetable tray and grill for a further 2 to 3 minutes until the trout flakes easily when you press it with a fork and the vegetables are blistered and really hot. Serve straight away.

Cajun-style Salmon Fillets

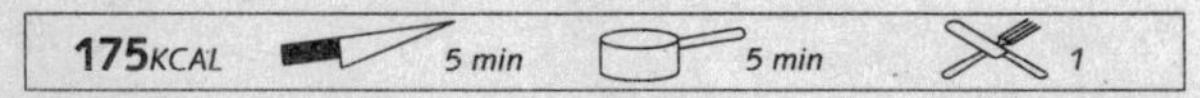

This is a great way to serve salmon – peppery on the outside and moist in the middle. If you are cooking for one, salmon isn't an outrageous expense any more and, with a fillet, you have the satisfaction of no fuss, no smell, no bones and no waste. Salmon contains its own natural oils so you need only the merest hint of oil in a non-stick pan to stop it sticking. Serve with very lightly boiled mangetout or broccoli and some boiled new potatoes. Or serve with some plain boiled rice and a big salad of young spinach leaves and slices of raw baby courgette.

2 teaspoons fresh marjoram leaves
¼ teaspoon ground black pepper
¼ teaspoon hot paprika pepper
75g (3oz) boneless, skinless salmon fillet
⅛ teaspoon olive oil
¼ very small lemon

1 Strip the marjoram leaves off the stem and finely chop. Mix in the black pepper and the paprika pepper and rub over both sides of the salmon.
2 Smear the oil in a shape the size of the salmon fillet in the middle of a small non-stick frying-pan with your finger. Place the pan over a medium heat.
3 Place the salmon on the oil and cook on one side for 1½ minutes then turn over and cook the second side for 1½ minutes. Reduce the heat, cover the pan and cook for a further 2 minutes until cooked through. (The salmon is cooked when the fish in the centre of the fillet flakes easily with a fork and is a cloudy pink all the way through.)
4 Squeeze the juice from the lemon wedge over the fillet and serve hot.

Smoked Haddock Fishcakes

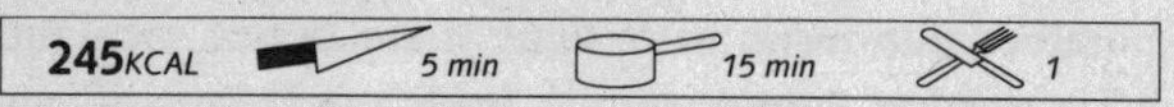

I love smoked haddock. We had it once a week when we were growing up and it was always a special treat if we went to stay with my Granny in Fraserburgh or my Aunt in Aberdeen. Both towns used to be important fishing ports in Scotland, with the local catch for sale on the quayside. We would always have haddock cooked gently in milk with an egg cracked into the cooking juices to poach along side the fish, and this is still one of my favourite suppers. Another favourite is this recipe blending smoked haddock with mashed potato to make a flavoursome fish cake. Simple and truly delicious. Serve with some lightly boiled green vegetables such as broccoli or green beans.

150g (6oz) potato
25g (1oz) from a small leek
100g (4oz) undyed smoked haddock fillet
50g (2oz) canned sweetcorn (drained weight)
ground black pepper
½ teaspoon olive oil

1 Thinly peel the potato and cut into small cubes. Place in a small saucepan and cover with cold water. Bring to the boil, reduce the heat to a simmer and cook for 5 minutes.
2 Meanwhile, rinse and finely chop the leek. Place

the fish on top of the potatoes when they have cooked for 5 minutes. Cover the pan and simmer for a further 3 minutes or until the potatoes feel soft when you prod them with a knife and the fish flakes easily.

3 Lift the fish out with a slotted spoon and keep on one side. Drain the potatoes and mash well. (Push though a sieve if you want really creamy potato.) Add the leek, the fish, the sweetcorn and some ground black pepper and stir to mix. On a flat plate or board, shape the mixture into a flat, round cake about 14cm (4in) across.

4 Heat the oil in a small non-stick frying-pan. Slide the fish cake into the pan and cook over a medium heat for 2 minutes without disturbing the bottom. Shake the pan to loosen the base, which should be golden and crusty, and slide the fish cake onto a serving plate. Flip the fish cake back into the frying-pan so that the golden side is up.

5 Cook for a further 2 minutes until the other side is golden and the fishcake is heated through. Slide onto a serving plate and serve hot.

- Sometimes, it's not what you eat but how much that is the problem. If you feel you already follow a low fat, high fibre diet then you need to eat less or exercise more. Eat more vegetables to fill you up.

Plaice Baked with Mushrooms and Tomatoes

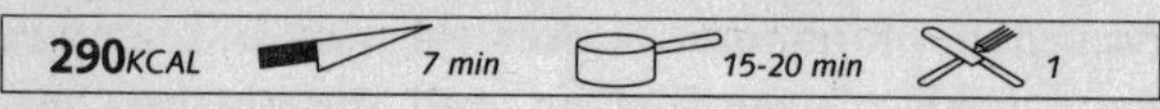

Plaice is a very fine-textured fish and fillets are absolutely bone free. It is quick to cook and, baked in the oven with a parsley and lemon stuffing, it makes an easy but very delicious supper. Serve with some crusty bread warmed through in the oven as you cook the fish and with a dark green salad – try watercress and young baby spinach leaves mixed together.

1 stick of celery
1 slice wholemeal bread weighing 25g (1oz)
½ small lemon
1 teaspoon walnut oil
1 tablespoon chopped fresh parsley
1 small skinless plaice fillet weighing 100g (4oz)
2 cocktail sticks
2 large flat mushrooms
1 beefsteak tomato
ground black pepper

1 Pre-heat the oven to its highest setting. Chop the celery very finely. Grate the bread on the coarse side of a grater to make crumbs. Finely grate the rind from the lemon and squeeze out the juice.
2 Heat the walnut oil in a small non-stick pan. Add the celery, the breadcrumbs and ½ teaspoon of the lemon rind. Stir-fry over a medium heat for 2 to 3

minutes until the crumbs are light golden. Remove from heat and stir in the parsley.

3 Cut the plaice fillet in half lengthways and arrange, skinned side down, on the work surface.

4 Spoon some of the breadcrumb mixture onto the plaice and roll each up. Secure the ends with a cocktail stick.

5 Wipe the mushrooms and remove the stalks. Cut the tomato in half round its middle.

6 Arrange the mushrooms in an ovenproof serving dish and arrange the plaice fillets on top of them. Add the tomatoes and season everything with pepper. Sprinkle the plaice with lemon juice and pile the rest of the stuffing mixture over the tomato halves. Add 1 tablespoon of water to each mushroom cap.

7 Bake for 12 to 15 minutes or until the fish is white all the way through and flakes easily if you prod it with a knife. Serve straight away.

- If you have a craving for something you are trying to cut down on then go ahead, have some of it – it's not totally banned. But be discerning – don't eat half a packet of Rich Tea biscuits when all you really want is one or two of the Bourbon Creams you are yearning for. Have a little of what you like and sit down, relax and enjoy it without overdoing it, rather than a lot of what you don't particularly want.

Grilled Chinese-glazed Haddock

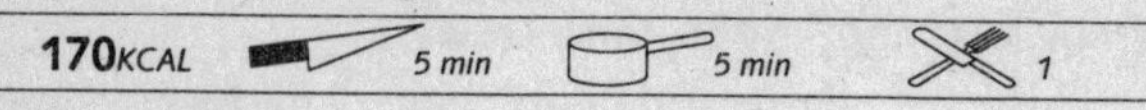

This sticky, shiny sauce for haddock or any other firm white fish, has the distinctly Chinese flavours of five-spice powder and hoisin sauce. If you have time, make it in the morning and leave the fish to sit in the marinade, covered in the fridge all day.

1 clove of garlic
2 teaspoons dark soy sauce
2 teaspoons hoisin sauce
½ teaspoon honey
good pinch five-spice powder
½ teaspoon sesame oil
125g (5oz) piece of skinless haddock fillet

1 Pre-heat the grill to its highest setting. Peel and crush the garlic. Place on a side plate with the soy sauce, hoisin sauce, honey and five-spice powder. Stir well so that everything is mixed.
2 Lay the haddock in the mixture and then turn it over so that it is well coated and there's not much mixture left on the plate.
3 Line a baking sheet with foil and oil part of the foil with the sesame oil. Place haddock on this and grill for 3 to 4 minutes or until the fish flakes easily when it is pressed with a fork.
4 Transfer to serving plate and eat straight away.

Roasted Prawns with Shiny Orange Sauce

This dish has a creamy, shiny sauce which is good served with pasta or vegetables like asparagus, young courgettes and mangetout. Look out for green, uncooked prawns. If they are pink when you buy them, they have already been cooked and further cooking will only toughen them. If you can't find the right sort of prawns, then try this sauce over a firm white fish like monkfish.

8 small chestnut or button mushrooms
2 satsumas or other small thin-skinned oranges
1 teaspoon olive oil
6 large, shelled, uncooked prawns weighing 175g (6oz)
1 teaspoon dark soy sauce
2 tablespoons Greek yoghurt

1 Wipe the mushrooms and cut in half. Squeeze the juice from the satsumas.
2 Heat the oil in a small non-stick frying-pan. Add the mushrooms and cook quickly, stirring, over a high heat for 2 minutes until mushrooms are golden.
3 Add the prawns and stir for 30 seconds. Add the juice from the satsumas and the soy sauce. Bring to the boil and simmer for 2 minutes.
4 Add the yoghurt and stir until the mixture has reduced to a shiny, coating sauce. Serve hot.

MAIN MEALS – CHICKEN AND TURKEY

Chicken is a lean, low fat meat.

It has got to be the most popular meat around and for good reason. It is still relatively cheap, it is quick to cook, easy to eat and popular with all ages. From a calorie point of view it is a lean, low fat meat. But be warned – do not eat the skin. All the fat is stored just underneath the skin and, even crisply roasted, the skin can add as much as half as many extra calories again to the dish. Wouldn't you rather have those calories as a pudding instead? There is no difference in calories between a battery bird and one that's been allowed to roam about or a difference between a pellet-fed chicken or one that's been corn fed. If you prefer the darker meat from the legs, it has slightly more calories weight for weight than meat from the breast or thigh but either way, chicken or turkey are still the number one choice for a low calorie, meaty meal.

From a flavour point of view, I think fresh chicken or turkey is definitely better than frozen. Boneless, skinless breasts make great burgers and stir-fries. Chicken on the bone has a sweeter flavour so use it for roasts, grills and barbecues with finger-licking sauces. Ideologically, free range birds are better than battery-reared ones but whether you can tell the difference in flavour once they are in a sauce or flavoured with herbs I think is debatable.

There is a large range of turkey cuts available

and they can be swapped for the chicken in these recipes for about the same number of calories – check the charts on page 40. Turkey can be dry, so cook it quickly, serve it with a flavoursome sauce like the one in the *Glazed Chicken in Orange Sauce* recipe (see page 239) or try my recipe for *Turkey with a Blue Cheese Filling* (see page 242).

Chicken Fajitas

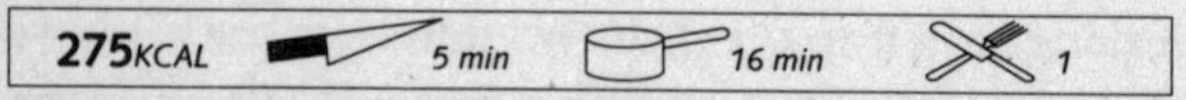

Pronounced fa-heet-as, this is a Mexican way of serving chicken. I first discovered it one sunny winter, on maternity leave, in Los Angeles. To make this, I have a jar of ready-mixed red and black pepper found in the spices section at the supermarket. It is wonderful sprinkled onto a number of dishes, but it is essential for this dish. If you can't find it, mix ground black pepper with equal quantities of ground paprika.

Traditionally this mixture is served in floury tortillas – thin flour pancakes a bit like the ones you get in Chinese restaurants if you order *Peking Duck*. They are difficult to get hold of, although some large supermarkets now stock them. They're not easy to make at home either unless you have the right flour. I improvise with a warmed, split pitta bread. If you like, at the end of the chicken's cooking time, heat half a wholemeal pitta bread through in the toaster, split and fill with the mixture (see Calorie Charts on page 36).

1 small red pepper
1 small onion
⅛ teaspoon mixed ground red and black pepper
2 teaspoons fresh oregano leaves
75g (3oz) boneless, skinless chicken breast
1 teaspoon olive oil
1 tablespoon Greek yoghurt

1 Halve and deseed the pepper and cut the flesh into strips. Peel, halve and slice the onion.
2 Mix the ground pepper and oregano together and rub all over the chicken. Cut the chicken into strips.
3 Heat the oil in a small, non-stick frying-pan. Add the chicken and cook for 30 seconds. Turn over and cook the second side until the chicken is slightly golden.
4 Add the onions and toss for 3 minutes.
5 Add the peppers. Cover with a lid, reduce the heat and cook gently for 10 minutes until the onions are browned and the peppers have wilted. Shake the pan from time to time to prevent the onions from sticking.
6 Pile the mixture onto a serving plate, spoon the yoghurt over the top and serve hot.

Cuban Roast Chicken with Lime and Garlic

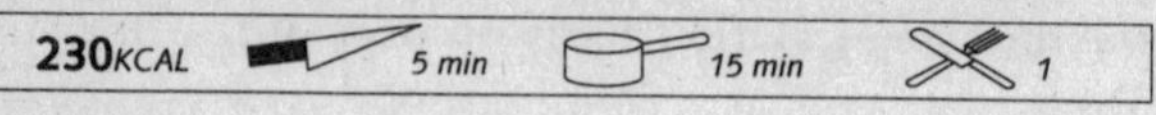

We were taken to a Cuban restaurant whilst in Los Angeles and all the food guides said to order this chicken dish. I did and it was delicious. This is my version, with the portions scaled down from regular American size, which was half a large chicken each. Delicious hot with a crisp green salad, cold for a lunch-box, or sometimes I roast some vegetables like peppers, courgettes and tomatoes while the oven or barbecue is hot.

½ lime
1 clove garlic
few drops Tabasco sauce or ¼ teaspoon sweet chilli sauce
1 chicken quarter, with skin and bones, weighing 285g (10oz)

1 Pre-heat the oven to its highest setting.
2 Finely grate the rind of the lime and squeeze the juice. Peel and crush the garlic.
3 Mix the lime rind and juice, garlic and Tabasco or sweet chilli sauce together.
4 Push your fingers between the flesh and the skin of the chicken. Work the skin loose at one end but don't pull it off, and leave one end with the skin still sealed. Spoon the lime mixture into the gap under the skin and fold the skin down over it to

stop the juices running out during the cooking.
5 Put the chicken on a rack in a small roasting tin. Bake, uncovered, for 20 minutes or until the skin is crispy and golden and the juices run clear when the chicken is prodded with a knife.
6 Pull off the chicken skin and discard. Serve hot.

Smoky Chicken Burgers

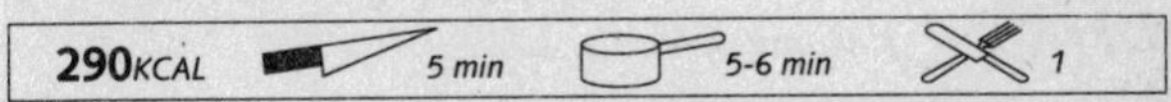

This makes a moist, smoky-flavoured, lean, meaty burger. Great to cook on the barbecue. Serve with a large, crunchy salad of lettuce, cherry tomatoes and strips of red pepper.

1 frankfurter
75g (3oz) boneless, skinless chicken breast
½ teaspoon olive oil

1 Roughly chop the frankfurter and the chicken. Place both in a food processor and pulse the machine until the mixture is roughly chopped.
2 Squeeze together and shape into a round burger about 7.5cm (3in) across.
3 Heat the oil in a non-stick frying-pan over a medium heat. Add the burger and fry for 2 minutes each side until browned. If the burger is not cooked through, reduce the heat, cover the pan with a lid and cook for a further 2 minutes. Serve hot.

Chicken with Mushrooms and Rosemary

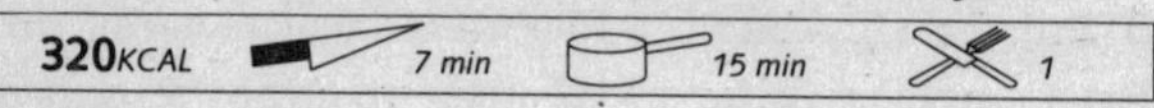

Chicken on the bone is much sweeter tasting than a boneless chicken breast, and the skin helps keep it moist. While the oven is on, I cook an extra portion of chicken in the roastabag to eat in a salad.

1 medium onion
225g (8oz) flat mushrooms
1 chicken quarter, with skin and bones, weighing 275g (10oz)
20 fresh rosemary leaves
salt
ground black pepper

1 Pre-heat the oven to its highest setting.
2 Peel and slice the onion. Wipe and thinly slice the mushrooms. Tip both into a roastabag and stand the bag in a small roasting tin.
3 Push your fingers under the skin of the chicken and work the skin loose. Don't pull it off.
4 Mix the rosemary with salt and pepper. Rub all over the chicken flesh, under the skin.
5 Place the chicken on top of the onion and mushrooms in the roastabag. Seal the bag loosely.
6 Cook for 20 minutes or until the chicken juices run clear when the flesh is prodded with a knife.
7 Pull off the chicken skin and discard. Serve the chicken hot with all the onions and mushrooms.

Glazed Chicken in Orange Sauce

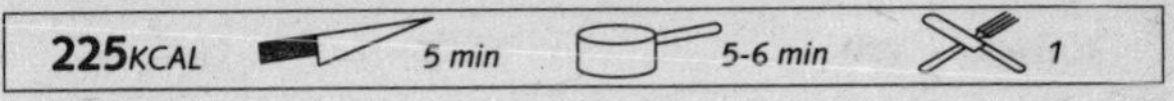

This recipe makes a generous quantity of tangy, orange-coloured sauce. Serve with steamed cauliflower, green beans and rings of tiny courgettes.

75g (3oz) boneless, skinless chicken breast
ground black pepper
½ teaspoon olive oil
1 teaspoon cornflour
1 large orange
1 tablespoon redcurrant or rowan jelly

1 Cut the chicken into strips and season lightly with pepper. Heat the oil in a small non-stick frying-pan over a medium heat.
2 Add the chicken. Cook for 30 seconds, turn and cook for a further 30 seconds. Reduce the heat, cover and cook for 2 minutes. Shake the pan, with the lid on, to prevent the chicken sticking.
3 Meanwhile, blend the cornflour with 2 teaspoons water. Finely grate the rind of the orange and squeeze the juice.
4 Add the orange rind and juice and the redcurrant jelly to the pan. Bring to the boil, stirring.
5 Remove from the heat and stir in the cornflour mixture. Return to the heat and bring to the boil, stirring to make a smooth shiny sauce. Simmer for 2 to 3 minutes until the chicken is cooked through.

Sticky Chicken Kebabs

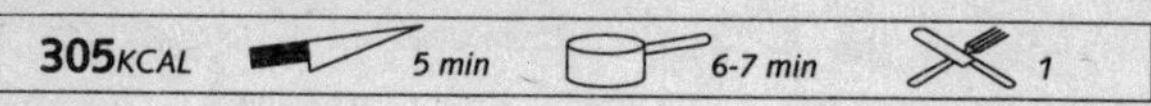

This is a great recipe to make at breakfast time and allow to marinade all day, not least because it has marmalade and orange juice in it. The onions, once they have been marinated and grilled, are really different to onions cooked any other way – crisp but sweet tasting. These kebabs are great cooked on the barbecue. Serve with a crisp green salad or a crunchy coleslaw.

75g (3oz) boneless, skinless chicken breast
2 very small onions (so that when they are quartered, they are about the same size as the mushrooms)
8 button mushrooms
1 tablespoon dark orange marmalade
1 tablespoon tomato ketchup
1 teaspoon Worcestershire sauce
1 tablespoon unsweetened fresh orange juice

1 Cut the chicken into 8 even-sized chunks. Peel the onion, but leave its root on, and cut into quarters. Wipe the mushrooms.
2 Spoon the marmalade, tomato ketchup, Worcestershire sauce and orange juice into a shallow mixing bowl. Add the chicken, onion and mushrooms and stir well to coat them. Cover and leave in the fridge for up to 1 day.
3 To cook, pre-heat the grill to its highest setting.

4 Thread the chicken, mushrooms and onions alternately on to 2 skewers and grill for 5 or 6 minutes, turning constantly, until golden.
5 Brush with any leftover marinade and grill for a further minute. Serve hot.

Chicken Tikka Kebabs

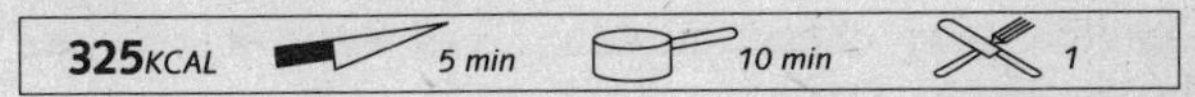

A quick but good version of this Indian favourite. Serve on a generous bed of shredded iceberg lettuce and sliced cucumber, with a wedge of fresh lemon.

3 boneless, skinless chicken thighs
3 tablespoons Greek yoghurt
1 teaspoon tikka paste or tandoori marinade
1 teaspoon tomato ketchup
1 tablespoon chopped fresh coriander leaves

1 Cut the chicken thighs in half.
2 Mix the yoghurt, tikka paste or tandoori marinade, tomato ketchup and fresh coriander together. Add the chicken pieces and toss to coat them completely. Cover with cling film and store in the fridge for at least 1 hour or for up to 1 day.
3 To cook pre-heat the grill to its highest setting. Thread the chicken pieces on to 2 skewers. Grill for 8 to 10 minutes, turning occasionally until evenly browned. (Alternatively, cook on the barbecue.)

Turkey with a Blue Cheese Filling

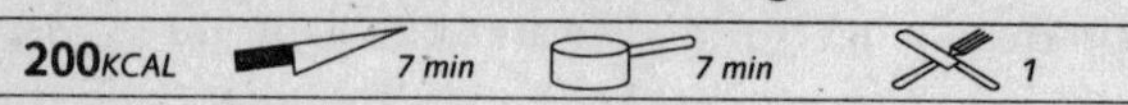

The inspiration for this recipe comes from a visit to an expensive French restaurant in Aberdeen. I was a student and my Mum and Dad were treating me. I ordered *Veal Danoise* which came in breadcrumbs, fried in butter. When I cut into the veal to reveal a melted blue cheese middle, I thought it was the most wonderful thing I'd ever eaten. From then on we used to make this dish as a celebration at the start of term before the grant ran out. We used pork fillet then, not veal, and now I make a healthy version – minus the breadcrumbs and the butter – using turkey. Turkey is cheap and low in fat, but can be dry unless you cook it properly. The blue cheese helps to keep the meat moist. I always cook some broccoli with this and serve with one or two tiny boiled new potatoes.

75g (3oz) turkey escalope
21g (¾oz) square of Danish blue cheese
1 teaspoon walnut oil
150ml (¼pt) half-strength chicken stock made with a cube

1 Cover the turkey with cling film and beat to a thin, flat square using a rolling pin.
2 Remove the film and arrange the blue cheese in the middle of one half of the turkey. Fold the

turkey over so the cheese is enclosed. Squash the cheese flat with your hand and roll the turkey with the rolling pin to flatten it slightly. Secure the ends with cocktail sticks.

3 Heat the oil in a small non-stick frying-pan and cook the turkey for 2 minutes on one side. Turn over and cook for 2 minutes on the other side. Reduce the heat, add the stock, cover the pan and cook gently for a further 2 minutes or until the turkey is cooked through.

4 Turn the heat back up and boil the stock rapidly for 2 to 3 minutes until there are only a couple of tablespoons left.

5 Slide onto a serving dish and pour the pan juice over the top.

- Don't ban foods – you'll just want to eat them all the more. No one food is bad for you. If it is high in fat or sugar then you just have to eat smaller quantities of it, less often.

MAIN MEALS – RED MEAT

The secret with meat is to trim off all the fat you see.

Lean red meat is a perfectly acceptable ingredient on your shopping list even if you are trying to cut back. The secret with meat as part of a calorie-controlled lifestyle is to trim off all the fat you can see. There is fat naturally marbled through the meat but this is what gives meat its flavour. If you do buy fattier meats like sausages, buy the extra lean sort, grill them well and prick them to let the extra fat run out. Buy mince that is labelled as extra lean and dry-fry it in its own fat to brown it. Remember fatty processed meats like economy sausages, salamis, shop-bought patés, corned beef and spam are high in fat and therefore high in calories and should be avoided. So, too, should any combination of meat and pastry.

Try to think about how much meat you eat. If you usually buy 450g (1lb) of mince to make a spaghetti bolognese-type recipe or chilli for two people, then you need to scale the meat down and increase the vegetables in order to eat the same quantity for fewer calories.

Lean beef has the lowest fat content and is your best bet, followed by lamb and then pork. If you are eating a roast, do trim off all the visible fat and don't eat the crackling on roast pork (or the Yorkshire puddings with the beef). Gravy should be unthickened and free of fat. While meat on the bone is more juicy, take care with chops to cut off the fatty outer rim after grilling. That way, when you chew the bones you won't be sucking in calories from the fatty skin.

Remember that the calorie counts given are for the recipe as it is written and do not include any serving suggestions.

Lamb with Orange and Redcurrant Sauce

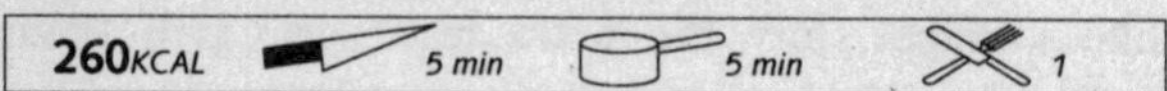

Look out for cartons of fresh concentrated stock now widely available in good supermarkets. Although expensive compared to a stock cube, they are great for this sort of sauce. I divide a tub into useful portions of 4 tablespoons. Using cling film, line a 12 hole bun tin (the sort with deep holes that you used to use to make Yorkshire puddings in). Spoon 4 tablespoonfuls of stock into each hole (it will probably give you 4 portions), cover and freeze. When you need a portion of stock, add it frozen to the pan. It will defrost very quickly.

The sauce for this can be made in advance and stored in the fridge for up to 2 days. Serve green vegetables like spinach, cabbage, green beans or broccoli (see Calorie Charts on page 60).

75g (3oz) fillet of lamb or lean leg steaks
ground black pepper
1 orange
1 tablespoon redcurrant or rowan jelly
1 teaspoon red wine vinegar
4 tablespoons fresh beef stock
1 teaspoon cornflour

1 Remove any fat from the lamb. Leave in one piece and season with pepper. Cut strips of rind from the orange, using an orange zester or canelle knife, and squeeze the juice.
2 Heat a small non-stick frying-pan over a medium heat. Add the lamb and dry-fry for 1 minute undisturbed. Turn over and cook for a further minute. Roll over to brown the sides.
3 Put the orange rind and juice in the pan with the redcurrant or rowan jelly, the vinegar and the stock. Bring to the boil, reduce the heat, cover and simmer for 1 minute.
4 Mix the cornflour with 2 teaspoons of water until smooth and stir into the hot liquid. Bring back to the boil, stirring all the time, until slightly thickened. Simmer for 1 minute.
5 Test the lamb for pinkness by cutting down through the middle with a sharp knife. Cook it for longer if you need to.
6 Remove the lamb from the pan and place it on your serving plate. Cut it into slices. Pour the sauce over the lamb and serve hot.

Lamb with Ginger, Mangetout and Spring Onions

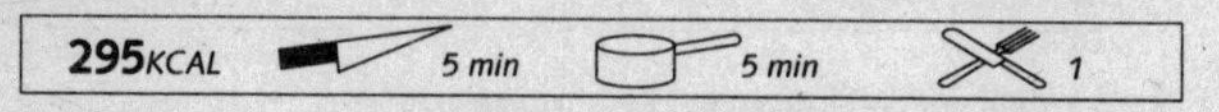

Almost every cut of lamb is quick to cook but the leg and the fillet are the leanest. I serve this with plain boiled rice. Try eating it with chopsticks to make it last longer.

75g (3oz) fillet of lamb or lean leg steaks
1cm (¼in) fresh root ginger
1 clove of garlic
2 spring onions
100g (4oz) fresh mangetout
½ teaspoon toasted sesame oil
⅛ teaspoon five-spice powder
1 teaspoon dark soy sauce

1 Slice the lamb thinly then cut into strips. Peel and finely shred the ginger. Peel and thinly slice the garlic and spring onion. Trim the mangetout and cut in half.
2 Heat the oil in a deep-sided, non-stick frying-pan and add the lamb, ginger, garlic, spring onions and the five-spice powder. Stir-fry for 1 to 2 minutes.
3 Add the mangetout, the soy sauce and 4 tablespoons of water and toss together, over a high heat, for a further 2 minutes. Tip immediately onto a serving plate and eat while piping hot.

Barbecued Pork

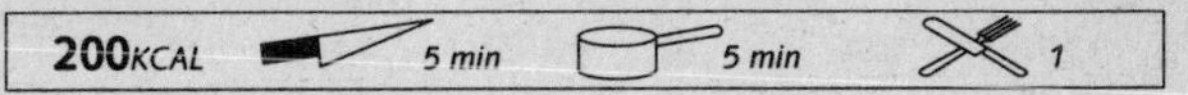

Mix the marinade in the morning if you can and leave the pork to soak up the flavours. A whole piece of pork fillet is wonderful marinated, barbecued and cut into thin slices. Serve with a stir-fry pack of fresh vegetables, some of those boil-and-soak instant egg noodles or plain boiled rice.

75g (3oz) pork fillet
1 tablespoon dark soy sauce
1 tablespoon bought hoisin sauce
1 teaspoon dry sherry
1 teaspoon well-flavoured clear honey
½ teaspoon sesame oil

1 Remove all the fat and any white stringy bits from the outside of the pork. Cut into thin slices.
2 Spoon the soy sauce, hoisin sauce, sherry and honey into a mixing bowl and stir together.
3 Add the pork and make sure it is well coated. (Cover and leave in the fridge for up to 1 day.)
4 Pre-heat the oil in a small non-stick frying-pan over a high heat. When it is hot, add the pork and fry for 1 minute on each side until it is browned.
5 Add the marinade ingredients and 4 tablespoons of water and allow to boil until the sauce has reduced back down to the original thickness of the marinade (before the water was added). Serve hot.

Pork with Parma Ham and Sage

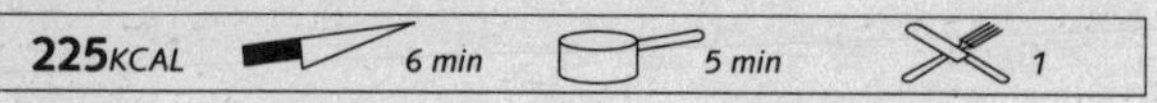

I think this is quite an elegant, sophisticated dish. Serve it with lightly cooked spinach, some courgette slices steamed until they are hot and some tiny new potatoes. You can always substitute a thin slice of lean, smoked ham for the parma ham if you like.

75g (3oz) pork fillet
1 slice parma ham
5 small fresh sage leaves
½ teaspoon olive oil
2 tablespoons medium dry sherry, like an oloroso

1 Remove all the fat and any white stringy bits from the outside of the pork. Score a cut lengthwise along the fillet and then cut inwards till you are half-way through. Open the fillet out flat, cover with cling film and beat to a thin, flat square using a rolling pin.
2 Remove the film and arrange the parma ham over the pork with the sage leaves on top. Fold the pork over so the ham and the leaves are enclosed. Roll the pork with the rolling pin to flatten it slightly and secure the ends with a cocktail stick.
3 Heat the oil in a small non-stick frying-pan over a medium heat. Add the pork and fry for 2 minutes on each side. Add the sherry and 4 tablespoons of water and allow it to boil for 1 minute. Reduce the

heat and cover the pan. Cook for a further 1 to 2 minutes, shaking pan occasionally, or until the pork is cooked through.

4 Slide the pork and the pan juices onto a serving plate and serve hot.

Mince with Mushrooms and Garlic

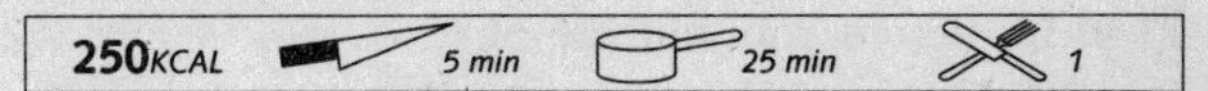

Choose extra lean mince – look out for the sort that's labelled less than 5% fat – and make two portions of this at a time if you can trust yourself to freeze one for another day. Serve this with lots of finely shredded steamed cabbage, steamed whole baby carrots and peas. If you top it with the *Celariac and Potato Purée with Nutmeg* (see recipe on page 174) or *Swede, Carrot and Tattie Mash* (see recipe on page 166), it makes a good cottage pie.

½ small onion
1 clove of garlic
50g (2oz) chestnut or brown cap mushrooms
1 teaspoon olive oil
75g (3oz) extra lean beef mince
2 teaspoons medium oatmeal
300ml (½pt) half-strength beef stock, made with a cube

Mince with Mushrooms and Garlic continued

1 Peel and finely chop the onion and the garlic. Wipe and roughly chop the mushrooms.

2 Heat the oil in a small non-stick saucepan over a high heat and add the onion, garlic and mushrooms. Stir-fry for 2 to 3 minutes, stirring well until the mushrooms are well browned and softened.

3 Add the mince a third at a time and brown each quantity before you add the next.

4 Add the oatmeal, stir well, then add the stock. Bring to the boil, turn the heat down, cover and simmer for 20 minutes or until the meat is tender.

5 Spoon onto serving plate with all the pan juices and eat while it's still hot.

Chilli Con Carne

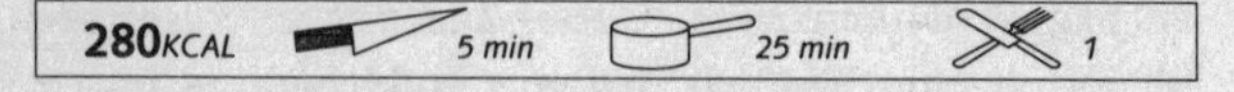

Look out for small, half-size cans of red kidney beans which are a good buy when you are cooking for one. What you don't use for this dish you can add to a salad with tuna, chopped onion and tomatoes. Try serving this with 25g (1oz) baked taco crisps (see Calorie Chart on page 41) or a small portion of plain rice and a lot of crisp shredded lettuce, diced ripe tomatoes and cucumber, tossed with a squeeze of lime juice.

½ small onion
1 clove of garlic
1 small green chilli
½ teaspoon olive oil
50g (2oz) extra lean minced beef
½ small green pepper
50g (2oz) canned red kidney beans, drained and rinsed
210g (7oz) can tomatoes
⅛ teaspoon ground nutmeg
Tabasco or other chilli sauce
250ml (½pt) half-strength beef stock made with a cube

1 Peel and finely chop the onion and the garlic. Halve and deseed the chilli and slice finely. Deseed the pepper and dice into small pieces.
2 Heat the oil in a non-stick saucepan over a high heat and add the onion, garlic and chilli. Stir-fry for 2 to 3 minutes, stirring well, until the onions are browned and softened.
3 Add the mince a third at a time and brown each quantity before you add the next.
4 Add the peppers, kidney beans, tomatoes, nutmeg, a good dash of chilli sauce and stock and stir well. Bring to the boil, turn the heat down, cover and simmer for 20 minutes or until the meat is tender.
5 Taste and add more chilli if you like. Spoon into a soup bowl with the pan juice and eat while it's hot.

Beef with Green Peppers and Black Beans

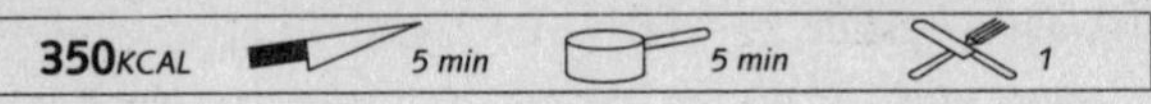

Fillet steak does seem an extravagance but because you are eating such a small amount you'll find that it'll cost you about the same as a frozen, calorie-counted meal. Fillet is the most tender cut of beef and will cook very quickly. Buy it from a good local butcher or, if you have a choice in the supermarket, spend extra on the traditionally reared variety as it usually has more flavour than the bright red, cheaper fillet. Serve with beansprouts, mixed half and half with coarsely grated carrots and lightly stir-fried, or some lightly boiled cauliflower or broccoli, or a small portion of plain boiled rice. The beef cooks very quickly so prepare these before you want to eat, and set the table before you start.

75g (3oz) fillet of beef
1cm (¼in) piece fresh root ginger weighing about 15g (½oz)
1 clove of garlic
1 spring onion
½ small green pepper
1 teaspoon dry sherry
2 tablespoons stir-fry black bean sauce
150ml (¼pt) water
1 teaspoon sesame oil

1 Thinly slice the beef. Peel and finely chop the ginger and the garlic. Strip the outer leaf from the spring onion, cut off the root and slice both the green and white parts into short lengths. Deseed the pepper and cut into small chunks.
2 Mix the dry sherry, black bean sauce and water together.
3 Heat the oil in a non-stick frying-pan over a high heat. Add the beef, ginger and garlic and stir-fry for 1 minute.
4 Add the spring onion, the green pepper and the black bean sauce mixture and stir well to mix.
5 Bring to the boil and cook rapidly, uncovered for 2 to 3 minutes.
6 Spoon onto a serving plate and eat while it's hot.

- The trick to low-calorie frying is to use a non-stick pan and heat it well with the measured amount of oil before adding the food. The hot oil seals the food, keeping the moisture in and giving the food a crispy outer.

PUDDINGS

These puds are designed to fill that end-of-meal gap.

There are times when a piece of fruit, however ripe or juicy, is just not enough to satisfy a craving for something sweet. The puddings in this chapter are designed to fill that gap. I'm not suggesting that you should have them at the end of every meal – although if you allow for them in your calorie count there's no reason why you shouldn't have them. Perhaps you will save them for a special meal like at the end of Sunday lunch, after a dinner on a Saturday night or for when you have friends round for supper. All of them will satisfy a sweet tooth as they are sweetened with things like mashed banana, maple syrup, ginger biscuits or sponge fingers. Where I've used sugar, it's been a small amount of unrefined soft brown sugar because it has more flavour than caster sugar and so you can use less of it to get the same amount of sweetness.

None of these desserts has cream in, yet some are really creamy and luxurious. The flavour and the texture comes from thick Greek yoghurt, medium fat fromage frais or smooth low fat soft cheeses. Nearly all include fruit, which is low in fat and therefore low in calories. One exception is *Tiramisu* see recipe on page 269) which is an Italian pudding of coffee-soaked sponge, layered with cream cheese and topped with a sprinkling of chocolate. My version of this has a calorie count you can afford. You won't find any fruit salads here because I've included lots of fruit salads and other fruity recipes in the Breakfast chapter. If you don't eat them at breakfast, then have them for lunch or as a pudding at night.

Banana and Coconut Brulée Ⓥ

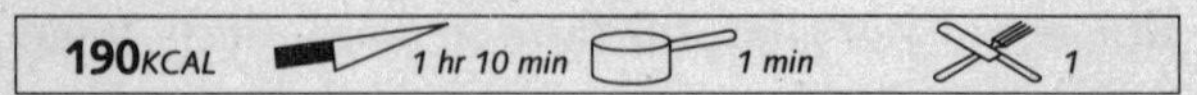

You get days when you need something sweet and if that's what your body wants then that's what your body should get. Don't resort to sweets and chocolate, try this first. This pudding does have a spoonful of sugar in it, but it is also naturally sweet from the bananas. It is truly scrumptious and I know someone who wouldn't eat a natural yoghurt and a banana if you paid him, who always enquires wistfully if there are any seconds when I make this. He has also been know to spread it on his toast instead of butter and marmalade at breakfast time.

several drops real vanilla essence
150g (5oz) carton low fat natural yoghurt
75g (3oz) banana, weighed after peeling
1 teaspoon desiccated coconut
1 teaspoon demerara sugar

1 Stir the vanilla essence into the carton of yoghurt. Line a nylon sieve with a piece of kitchen roll paper and stand over a bowl. Tip the yoghurt into it, cover and leave for at least 1 hour (or up to 8 hours in the fridge). Stir the set yoghurt from the outside into the middle from time to time if you can taking care not to tear the kitchen paper. The whey will collect in the jug and the yoghurt will have thickened and reduced to about 2 heaped tablespoonfuls.
2 Pre-heat the grill to its highest setting. Mash the banana until smooth.
3 Spoon the thickened yoghurt into a small ovenproof soufflé dish about 7.5cm (3in) in diameter. Spoon the banana over the yoghurt and gently spread to the edges. Sprinkle the coconut over and sprinkle the sugar on top.
4 Grill for 30 seconds or until the coconut begins to go golden and the sugar begins to melt. (Watch it carefully so the coconut doesn't burn.) Remove from the grill and allow to cool slightly before serving. Caution: the sugar topping will be very hot.

• Cream is a dietary no-no. Double cream is 48% fat, whipping cream is 35% fat and single cream is 18% fat. If you want something rich and creamy try Greek yogurt which is 8-10% fat or enjoy a flavoured fromage frais.

Mango Sorbet with Lemon and Lime Ⓥ

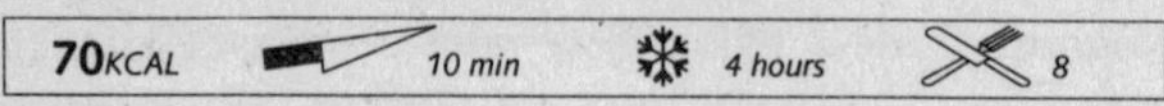

This is really quick to make and doesn't need any of the beating and freezing you usually require with home-made ices. It's a good standby to have in the freezer and cheaper than shop-bought sorbet. You can also use canned mangoes or canned peaches, without their juice. Take it out of the freezer 15 minutes before you need to serve it to make it easier to scoop. Serve with a sauce of puréed, sieved and warmed raspberries or in a *Brandy Snap Basket* (see recipe on page 266).

1 lime
1 large fresh mango weighing about 450g (1lb)
2 tablespoons fresh lemon juice
2 egg whites
50g (2oz) unrefined soft brown sugar

1 Finely grate rind from lime and squeeze out the juice. Halve the mango, slicing to one side of its flat stone, and scoop out the flesh with a teaspoon. Cut on the other side of the stone and repeat.
2 Place the mango, lime rind and juice in a liquidiser and add the lemon juice. Run the machine to make a smooth purée.
3 Whisk the egg whites in a clean grease-free bowl until they are stiff and dry. Add the sugar, a spoonful at a time, whisking well between each

addition to make a soft shiny meringue which falls in soft peaks when you lift the beaters out.

4 Fold the mango purée into the meringue using a metal spoon and stir gently to mix. Pour into a 1 litre (1¾pt) container and freeze until firm. Score into 8 portions with a knife.

Raspberry and Maple Layer Ⓥ

I adore raspberries and make this quick pudding when they are fresh in June, or I use frozen the rest of the year. If you don't have any maple syrup, use 1 teaspoon of well-flavoured clear honey.

125g (4oz) fresh or frozen raspberries
75g (3oz) thick Greek yoghurt
2 teaspoons real maple syrup
sprig of fresh mint to decorate (optional)

1 Hull the raspberries if fresh, allow to defrost if frozen. Put half in the bottom of a wine glass.

2 Mix the yoghurt with the maple syrup or honey and spoon half over the raspberries.

3 Reserve 2 raspberries for the top and layer the raspberries and the yoghurt mixture once more.

4 Top with the reserved raspberries and eat straight away or chill until needed. Add a sprig of fresh mint if you like before serving.

Ginger and Mango Cream Ⓥ

Choose a glass that's about the same diameter as the ginger nut biscuit for the best effect. Sometimes I make this with ripe fresh peaches or nectarines. Try this, too, with a medium-sized banana.

1 small fresh, ripe mango weighing 250g (9oz) with the skin and stone
1 teaspoon lemon or lime juice
4 tablespoons Greek yoghurt
3 Ginger Nut biscuits

1 Halve the mango, slicing to one side of its flat stone and scoop out the flesh from the skin with a teaspoon. You will need four tablespoons. Mash with a fork or liquidise until smooth. Stir in the lemon or lime juice.
2 Place 1 spoonful of yoghurt into straight-sided tumbler or a wine glass. Top with 1 spoonful of puréed mango and a ginger biscuit. Repeat the layers finishing with the mango. Allow to sit for at least 20 minutes or up to 1 day in the fridge.

Meringue with Vanilla Cream and Berries Ⓥ

Shop-bought meringue nests are a surprisingly low-calorie base for puddings, despite their sugar content. One small shop-bought meringue nest will have the same number of calories as a small pot of low fat yoghurt. Filled with a 'cream' and topped with fresh fruit, they make a satisfying and stylish pudding when you need something sweet. Bought meringues aren't as chewy as home-made ones so, if you want to avoid the meringue flying off your plate when you cut into it, let this soften for about 15 minutes before you eat it.

2 tablespoons thick natural yoghurt
2 tablespoon ready-made low fat custard
100g (4oz) fresh summer berries such as strawberries, raspberries, and redcurrants
1 shop-bought meringue nest

1 Mix the yoghurt with the custard.
2 Hull and halve the strawberries, hull the raspberries, and rinse the redcurrants.
3 Place the meringue on a small serving plate. Spoon the yoghurt mixture into the centre and top with some of the berries. Arrange the rest of the berries around the edge.

Apple and Hazelnut Layer with Nutmeg Ⓥ

This is something to eat as soon as it's made because the apple starts to go brown within about 15 minutes. It's ideal for a middle-of-the-week pudding and much more interesting than a yoghurt and apple eaten separately. Whole nutmeg stores well and gives a much fresher flavour, when freshly grated on the finest side of the grater, than the ready-ground version. No apologies for using sugar here – it's just right for flavour and texture.

4 toasted hazelnuts
4 tablespoons Greek yoghurt
4 tablespoons thick natural yoghurt
⅛ teaspoon of freshly ground nutmeg
1 tart eating apple
1 teaspoon demerara sugar

1 Finely chop the hazelnuts. Spoon the yoghurts into a small bowl. Finely grate the nutmeg and stir into the yoghurt.
2 Core the apple and halve. Hold the cut side to the grater and the skin side in your hand and grate coarsely up to the skin. Mix the apple, hazelnuts and demerara together in a small bowl.
3 Place a spoonful of yoghurt in the bottom of a wine glass, top with half the apple mixture and repeat the layers. Eat at once.

Lemon and Sultana Cheesecake Ⓥ

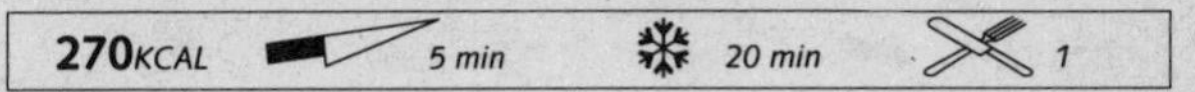

I do adore cheesecakes especially the really claggy, baked, continental sort that sticks to the roof of your mouth. This pud isn't quite in that category, but usually does the trick if I'm in need of an occasional splurge or something more substantial than a yoghurt.

½ small lemon
50g (2oz) smooth low fat soft cheese
2 tablespoons vanilla fromage frais
4 sponge fingers or 25g (1oz) fresh trifle sponge
15g (½oz) plump sultanas

1 Finely grate the rind from the lemon and squeeze out the juice.
2 Place 1 teaspoonful of the rind in a small bowl. Add the cheese and fromage frais and beat until smooth.
3 Place 2 teaspoons of lemon juice and 2 teaspoons of water on a small plate. Dip the sponge fingers or trifle sponge in the lemon juice mixture and arrange in the bottom of an individual glass serving dish.
4 Stir the sultanas into the cheese mixture and spoon on top. Smooth the top and allow to set in the fridge for 20 minutes.

Brandy Snap Basket Ⓥ

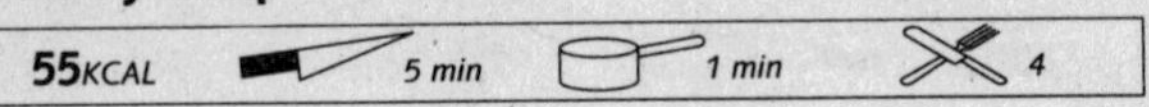

This is a handy trick if you need a low calorie pudding for a birthday or anniversary or if you are entertaining. Fill with the *Mango Sorbet with Lemon and Lime* (see recipe on page 260) or a shop-bought sorbet or low fat ice-cream, and decorate with fresh fruit.

4 bought brandy snaps
4 tall thin glass spice jars to mould the brandy snaps on

1 Pre-heat the grill to a medium setting. Place the brandy snaps, well spaced apart on a non-stick baking sheet.
2 Turn the spice jars upside down so that they are standing on their lids with their glass bottoms in the air.
3 Put the brandy snaps under the grill for 1 min until they soften and unroll. Watch them all the time.
4 When they have flattened to a soft circle, slip a palette knife underneath and drape them over the spice jars. Pinch the edges a little to make upside down baskets. Allow to cool.
5 When hardened, free the spice jars, turn brandy snaps over and arrange on a serving plate. Fill with sorbet and decorate with fresh fruit of your choice.

Layered Summer Pudding Ⓥ

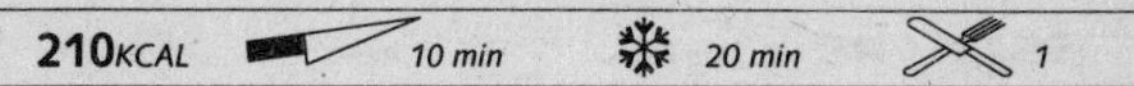

Traditionally made with white bread, I like this classic pudding made with good wholemeal bread from the health food shop or a good baker. Please don't use ready sliced mass-produced white bread for this because it goes slimy. Look out for bags of frozen mixed berries – cherries, strawberries, raspberries, blackcurrants – available in all major supermarkets now. What you don't use for this pudding you can have for breakfast with some yoghurt or fromage frais.

1 small thin slice wholemeal bread weighing 25g (1oz)
100g (4oz) frozen mixed summer fruits, defrosted
1 teaspoon unrefined soft brown sugar

1 Cut the crusts off the bread. Cut out three circles the same size as a small ramekin or mini soufflé dish. Arrange one circle on the bottom. Dip one circle in the juice from the fruits to colour it and set aside to use for the top.
2 Mix the fruits with the sugar and spoon half into the dish. Cover with the second round of bread and the rest of the fruit. Top with juice-soaked bread and pour any juice from the fruit over the top.
3 Cover with cling film and leave for at least 20 minutes before serving.

Creme Brulée with Raspberries Ⓥ

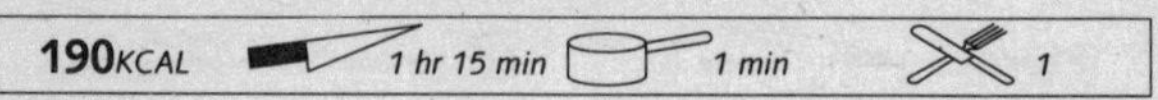

This is one of those puddings which is easy to make but does need a little planning. The secret lies in the wonderful thickened yoghurt which you have to allow to drain. I prepare the yoghurt and leave it in the fridge in the morning before I go to work. When I come home I just assemble and grill.

several drops real vanilla essence
150g (5oz) carton low fat natural yoghurt
100g (4oz) raspberries
1 teaspoon demerara sugar

1 Stir the vanilla essence into the yoghurt. Line a sieve with a piece of kitchen roll and stand over a bowl. Tip the yoghurt into it, cover and leave for at least 1 hour (or up to 8 hours in the fridge). Stir the yoghurt from the outside into the middle from time to time if you can. The whey will collect in the jug and the yoghurt will have reduced to about 2 heaped tablespoonfuls.
2 Pre-heat the grill to its highest setting. Tip the raspberries into a small ovenproof soufflé dish about 7.5cm (3in) in diameter. Spoon the yoghurt over and spread to the edges. Sprinkle with sugar.
3 Grill for 1 minute or until the sugar begins to melt. (Watch it carefully so that it doesn't burn.) Allow to cool slightly before serving.

Tiramisu Ⓥ

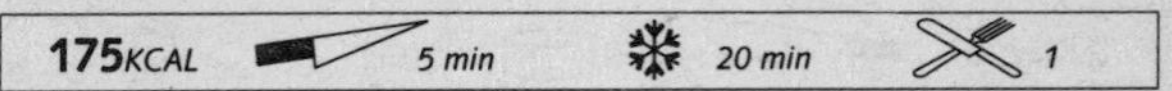

This is one of my favourite recipes – great for one and even better to serve to friends. And it's so easy to make that even beginners can put it together and be proud of the result. In an ideal world, you'd make this wonderful Italian pudding with real espresso coffee. I suspect most of us resort to instant. Use what's handy – the calorie count is the same.

2 tablespoons strong black coffee
4 sponge fingers
40g (1½oz) smooth low fat soft cheese
2 tablespoon thick Greek yoghurt
⅛ teaspoon drinking chocolate

1 Place the coffee in flat dish and dip the sponge fingers in. Break in half and press two halves into the bottom of a wine glass.
2 Beat the soft cheese and yoghurt together until creamy. Spoon half over the sponge fingers. Add another coffee-dipped sponge finger and repeat the layers finishing with the yoghurt mixture.
3 Sprinkle the drinking chocolate on top and chill for 20 minutes or up to 1 day.

Bramble and Apple with Pumpernickel Ⓥ

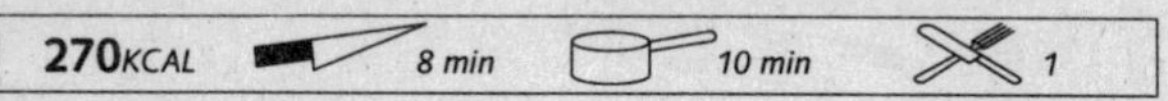

I love brambles and apples together, although it's years since I've been for a country walk clutching a carrier bag to put the precious berries in. These days its quicker and easier to buy them as cultivated blackberries although, perhaps nostalgically, I think the flavour is not the same.

1 clementine or other small thin-skinned orange
1 small sweet eating apple like a Cox's Orange Pippin
125g (4oz) brambles or blackberries
1 slice pumpernickel weighing 25g (1oz)
2 tablespoons Greek yoghurt

1 Finely grate the rind from the clementine and squeeze out the juice.
2 Peel, core and slice the apple into a small pan. Add the clementine juice and the brambles or blackberries. Bring to the boil, reduce the heat, cover and simmer for 10 minutes. Mash with a fork and sieve. Discard the pips and bits in the sieve.
3 Tear pumpernickel into small pieces and reduce to breadcrumbs in a food processor.
4 Spoon a third of the apple purée into a glass. Top with a third of the pumpernickel and repeat the layers finishing with the pumpernickel.
5 Stir the clementine rind into the yoghurt and spoon over the top to cover. Eat while warm or chill.